Spelling Connections

TEXAS Edition 1

J. Richard Gentry, Ph.D.

Zaner-Bloser

Author
J. Richard Gentry, Ph. D.

Reviewers
Paula Boales, Killeen ISD, Killeen, TX
Sherry Durham, Ed. D., Lufkin ISD, Lufkin, TX
Karyn L. Huskisson, Klein Instructional Center, Spring, TX
Carmen Ramos, San Benito CISD, San Benito, TX
Susan Shogan, Round Rock ISD, Round Rock, TX
Linda Stout, Crawford ISD, Crawford, TX

ELL and Spanish Consultants
Ellen Riojas Clark, Ph.D., Professor, College of Education and Human
   Development, Division of Bicultural-Bilingual Studies, The University of
   Texas at San Antonio, TX
Bertha Pérez, Ed.D., Professor Emeritus of Literacy, College of Education
   and Human Development, The University of Texas at San Antonio, TX
Rocio Reyes-Moore, Spanish Language Productions, Alexandria, OH

ISBN 978-0-7367-6866-5

Copyright © 2012 Zaner-Bloser, Inc.

Zaner-Bloser, Inc.
1-800-421-3018
www.zaner-bloser.com
Printed in the United States of America   13 14 15 16 17 330 10 9 8 7 6

SUSTAINABLE FORESTRY INITIATIVE

Certified Chain of Custody
Promoting Sustainable Forestry
www.sfiprogram.org
SFI-01042

Table of Contents

Bonus Pages:
My Spelling Dictionary

My Spelling Dictionary Front Cover
High Frequency Writing Words/
   Manuscript Alphabet Back Cover

Alphabet and Picture Cards

Word Sorting

A word sort helps you see how words are the same. The words **hat, sat,** and **mat** go together in a word sort. They all have the letters **at**. Word sorting can help you remember how to spell words.

There are different kinds of word sorts you can use with your spelling words.

- **Individual Sort**—Sort your words by yourself.
- **Buddy Sort**—Sort with a partner.
- **Speed Sorts on Your Own**—Time yourself as you sort your words. Then start over and try to get faster!
- **Speed Sorts With a Team**—See which team can sort the fastest and with the most right answers.

Buddy Sort using the word sort cards

Word sort on an interactive whiteboard

Spell Check

When you write on a computer, spell check can help you find spelling mistakes.

If you type **yuo** when you meant to type **you,** then spell check will let you know you made a mistake. It will even ask if you meant to type **you**.

But if you type **sick** and you meant to type **sock,** spell check cannot help. Why? Because **sick** and **sock** are both words, and spell check doesn't know you typed the wrong word.

Spell check helps find misspelled words.

Taking a Test

1 **Get** ready for the test. Have your paper and pencil ready.

2 **Listen** to your teacher say the word and use it in a sentence.

3 **Write** the word. Use your best handwriting.

4 **Check** your words with your teacher. Listen to your teacher say the word. Say the word aloud.

5 **Listen** to your teacher spell the word.

6 **Put** a check above each correct letter. Circle a letter that is not correct.

7 **Write** each misspelled word correctly. Say the word. Say each letter out loud.

Identifying Initial Sounds

Say the name of this picture:  .

Circle the pictures that start with the same sound.

 Help your child name other words that start like **tent**.

Phonemic Awareness

Recognizing Rhyme

Say the name of this picture:  .

Say the name of each picture below. Circle the pictures that rhyme with **cat**.

Counting Sounds in Words

Say the name of this picture: 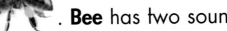. **Bee** has two sounds.

Say the first sound in **bee**. Say the second sound in **bee**.

Say the name of this picture: . **Bean** has three sounds.

Circle the picture in each pair that has two sounds.

 Make a list of simple words. Take turns with your child. One of you says a word, and one of you tells the number of sounds in the word.

Phonemic Awareness

Counting Sounds in Words

Say: bag. Say the first sound in **bag**. Say the second sound in **bag**. Say the third sound in **bag**. **Bag** has three sounds. Say the name of each picture. Circle the pictures with names that have three sounds.

● Say the name of each picture.
Circle the pictures that begin with **b** like **ball**.

■ Write **b** to complete each word.

_____ ee   _____ ox   _____ us

▲ Trace. Practice.

School Home This page provides practice with the sound of initial **Bb**. Help your child name the pictures and practice writing the letter.

TEKS 1.22A Use phonological knowledge to match sounds to letters to construct known words.

Cc

Sounds and Letters

● Say the name of each picture.
Circle the pictures that begin with **c** like **cat**.

■ Write **c** to complete each word.

____up   ____ub   ____ar

▲ Trace. Practice.

C C

c c

This page provides practice with the sound of initial **Cc**. Help your child name the pictures and practice writing the letter.

18

TEKS 1.22A Use phonological knowledge to match sounds to letters to construct known words.

● Say the name of each picture.
Circle the pictures that begin with **d** like **desk**.

■ Write **d** to complete each word.

___eer ___ish ___og

▲ Trace. Practice.

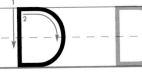 D D

 d d

 This page provides practice with the sound of initial **Dd**. Help your child name the pictures and practice writing the letter.

TEKS 1.22A Use phonological knowledge to match sounds to letters to construct known words.

● Look at each picture and say its name.
Draw a box around the pictures that begin with **f** like **fish**.

■ Write **f** to complete each word.

_____ork   _____ive   _____ox

▲ Trace. Practice.

F F

f f

  This page provides practice with the sound of initial **Ff**. Help your child name the pictures and practice writing the letter.

 TEKS 1.22A Use phonological knowledge to match sounds to letters to construct known words.

● Say the name of each picture.
Circle the pictures that begin with **g** like  **gate**.

■ Write **g** to complete each word.

irl   oat   um

▲ Trace. Practice.

G G

g g

 This page provides practice with the sound of initial **Gg**. Help your child name the pictures and practice writing the letter.

 TEKS 1.22A Use phonological knowledge to match sounds to letters to construct known words.

● Say the name of each picture.
  Color the pictures that begin with **h** like **heart**.

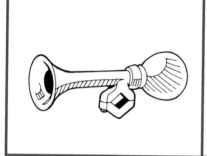 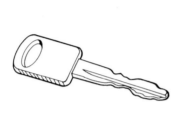 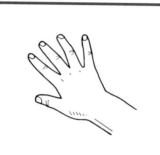 

■ Write **h** to complete each word.

_____orn   _____and   _____at

▲ Trace. Practice.

 This page provides practice with the sound of initial **Hh**. Help your child name the pictures and practice writing the letter.

TEKS 1.22A Use phonological knowledge to match sounds to letters to construct known words.

● Say the name of each picture.
Draw a ✓ under the pictures that begin with **j** like **jam**.

■ Write **j** to complete each word.

___ ar ___ et ___ eep

▲ Trace. Practice.

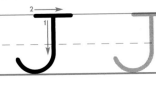

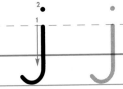

 This page provides practice with the sound of initial **Jj**. Help your child name the pictures and practice writing the letter.

 TEKS 1.22A Use phonological knowledge to match sounds to letters to construct known words.

 Sounds and **Letters**

● Say the name of each picture.
Draw a line under the pictures that begin with **k** like  **kitten**.

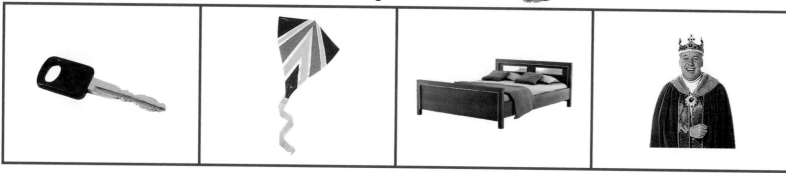

■ Write **k** to complete each word.

_____ey   _____ite   _____ing

▲ Trace. Practice.

 K K

 k k

 School Home
This page provides practice with the sound of initial **Kk**. Help your child name the pictures and practice writing the letter.

TEKS 1.22A Use phonological knowledge to match sounds to letters to construct known words.

● Look at each picture and say its name.
  Draw a box around the pictures that begin with **l** like **lion**.

■ Write **l** to complete each word.

_____ eaf   _____ ake   _____ ips

▲ Trace. Practice.

 This page provides practice with the sound of initial **Ll**. Help
your child name the pictures and practice writing the letter.

 TEKS 1.22A Use phonological knowledge to match sounds to letters to construct known words.

● Look at each picture and say its name.
Circle the pictures that begin with **m** like **men**.

■ Write **m** to complete each word.

_____ an   _____ op   _____ eat

▲ Trace. Practice.

M M

m m

 This page provides practice with the sound of initial **Mm**. Help your child name the pictures and practice writing the letter.

TEKS 1.22A Use phonological knowledge to match sounds to letters to construct known words.

● Look at each picture and say its name.
Draw a line under the pictures that begin with **n** like  **nine**.

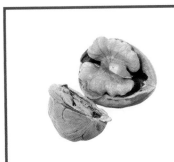   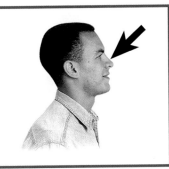

■ Write **n** to complete each word.

_ut   _est   _ose

▲ Trace. Practice.

 This page provides practice with the sound of initial **Nn**. Help
your child name the pictures and practice writing the letter.

 TEKS 1.22A Use phonological knowledge to match sounds to letters to construct known words.

Pp

● Say the name of each picture.

Circle the pictures that begin with **p** like **pot**.

■ Write **p** to complete each word.

en   aw   ie

▲ Trace. Practice.

 P   P

 p   p

 School Home This page provides practice with the sound of initial **Pp**. Help your child name the pictures and practice writing the letter.

TEKS 1.22A Use phonological knowledge to match sounds to letters to construct known words.

● Say the name of each picture.
Draw a box around the pictures that begin with **q** like **quarter**.

■ Write **q** to complete each word.

ueen   uack   uilt

▲ Trace. Practice.

 This page provides practice with the sound of initial **Qq**. Help
your child name the pictures and practice writing the letter.

 TEKS 1.22A Use phonological knowledge to match sounds to letters to construct known words.

● Look at each picture and say its name.
Color the pictures that begin with **r** like **rock**.

■ Write **r** to complete each word.

_____ope   _____ake   _____ing

▲ Trace. Practice.

R R

r r

 This page provides practice with the sound of initial **Rr**. Help
your child name the pictures and practice writing the letter.

TEKS 1.22A Use phonological knowledge to match sounds to letters to construct known words.

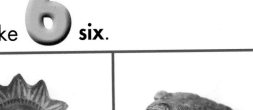

● Look at each picture and say its name.
Draw a line under the pictures that begin with **s** like **6** **six**.

■ Write **s** to complete each word.

ail   ock   un

▲ Trace. Practice.

S S

s s

 This page provides practice with the sound of initial **Ss**. Help your child name the pictures and practice writing the letter.

31

 TEKS 1.22A Use phonological knowledge to match sounds to letters to construct known words.

● Listen as you say the name of each picture.
Circle the pictures that begin with **t** like ➡ **tail**.

	**10**		

■ Write **t** to complete each word.

_____op   _____en   _____oys

▲ Trace. Practice.

 /
This page provides practice with the sound of initial **Tt**. Help
your child name the pictures and practice writing the letter.

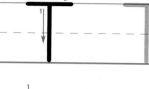 **TEKS 1.22A** Use phonological knowledge to match sounds to letters to construct known words.

Sounds and Letters

Vv

● Say the name of each picture.
Draw a ✓ under the pictures that begin with **v** like **vest**.

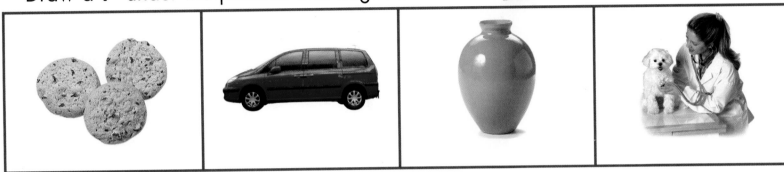

■ Write **v** to complete each word.

___an   ___ase   ___et

▲ Trace. Practice.

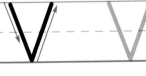

This page provides practice with the sound of initial **Vv**. Help your child name the pictures and practice writing the letter.

TEKS 1.22A Use phonological knowledge to match sounds to letters to construct known words.

Ww

Sounds and Letters

● Say the name of each picture.
Draw a box around the pictures that begin with **w** like **watch**.

■ Write **w** to complete each word.

_____eb   _____orm   _____ave

▲ Trace. Practice.

TEKS 1.22A Use phonological knowledge to match sounds to letters to construct known words.

● Say the name of each picture.
   Color the pictures that end with **x** like **box**.

■ Write **x** to complete each word.

fo _____   a _____   o _____

▲ Trace. Practice.

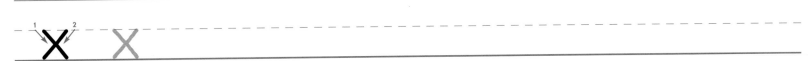

This page provides practice with the sound of final **Xx**. Help
your child name the pictures and practice writing the letter.

 TEKS 1.22A Use phonological knowledge to match sounds to letters to construct known words.

Yy

 **Sounds** and **Letters**

● Look at each picture and say its name.
Draw a ✓ under the pictures that begin with **y** like 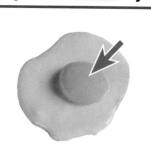 **yellow**.

 |  | |

■ Write **y** to complete each word.

___arn   ___olk   ___ell

▲ Trace. Practice.

 Y Y

 y y

This page provides practice with the sound of initial **Yy**. Help
your child name the pictures and practice writing the letter.

TEKS 1.22A Use phonological knowledge to match sounds to letters to construct known words.

● Look at each picture and say its name.
Draw a box around the pictures that begin with **z** like **zipper**.

■ Write **z** to complete each word.

ebra ⎯⎯⎯ oo ⎯⎯⎯ ero

▲ Trace. Practice.

Z Z

z z

 This page provides practice with the sound of initial **Zz**. Help your child name the pictures and practice writing the letter.

 TEKS 1.22A Use phonological knowledge to match sounds to letters to construct known words.

 **Aa**

 Sounds and Letters

● Look at each picture and say its name.
Draw a ✓ under the pictures that begin with **a** like **apple**.

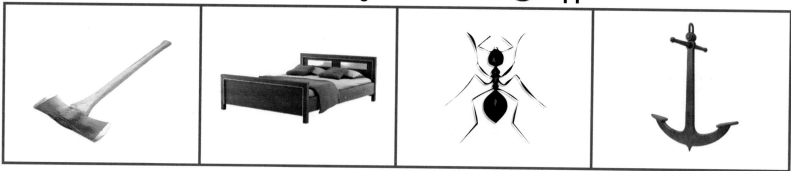

■ Write **a** to complete each word.

_____ x   _____ nt   _____ nchor

▲ Trace. Practice.

 A A

 a a

 School Home This page provides practice with the sound of initial **Aa**. Help your child name the pictures and practice writing the letter.

TEKS 1.22A Use phonological knowledge to match sounds to letters to construct known words.

● Look at each picture and say its name.
Circle the pictures that begin with **e** like **exit**.

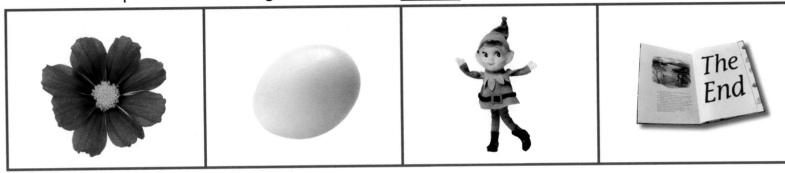

■ Write **e** to complete each word.

gg | lf | nd

▲ Trace. Practice.

E E

e e

 This page provides practice with the sound of initial **Ee**. Help your child name the pictures and practice writing the letter.

 TEKS 1.22A Use phonological knowledge to match sounds to letters to construct known words.

● Say the name of each picture.

Color the pictures that begin with **i** like **igloo**.

■ Write **i** to complete each word.

nch　　　　　　nk　　nsect

▲ Trace. Practice.

This page provides practice with the sound of initial **Ii**. Help
your child name the pictures and practice writing the letter.

TEKS 1.22A Use phonological knowledge to match sounds to letters to construct known words.

● Say the name of each picture.
Circle the pictures that begin with **o** like  **ostrich**.

■ Write **o** to complete each word.

 live   x   ff

▲ Trace. Practice.

 This page provides practice with the sound of initial **Oo**. Help your child name the pictures and practice writing the letter.

 TEKS 1.22A Use phonological knowledge to match sounds to letters to construct known words.

 **Uu**

● Say the name of each picture.

Color the pictures that begin with **u** like **umbrella**.

 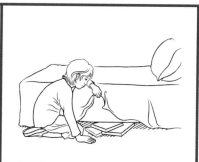 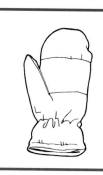 

■ Write **u** to complete each word.

p   nder   mpire

▲ Trace. Practice.

 This page provides practice with the sound of initial **Uu**. Help
your child name the pictures and practice writing the letter.

TEKS 1.22A Use phonological knowledge to match sounds to letters to construct known words.

1. an

2. can

3. man

4. ran

5. had

6. dad

A. Write the spelling words that end with **ad**.

1. _____ 2. _____

B. Write the spelling words that end with **an**.

3. _____ 4. _____

5. _____ 6. _____

School Home
This unit targets the **short a** sound. Ask your child to read the spelling words to you.

TEKS 1.22C Spell high-frequency words from a commonly used list.

A. Draw a line to match each spelling word with the picture name that begins with the same sound.

1. an   2. had   3. man   4. ran

an

can

man

ran

had

dad

B. Name each picture. Write the first letter of each picture name to make a spelling word.

5.

6.

7.

8.

9.

10.

TEKS 1.22A Use phonological knowledge to match sounds to letters to construct known words. **1.22C** Spell high-frequency words from a commonly used list.

Write a spelling word to complete each sentence.

an	can	dad

1. My _____ is a teacher.

2. I have _____ apple.

3. You _____ paint with me.

had	man	ran

4. We _____ to your house.

5. A _____ is on the swing.

6. The worm _____ a hat.

an

can

man

ran

had

dad

TEKS 1.22C Spell high-frequency words from a commonly used list.

Look at the picture. Use your spelling words to complete a story about the picture.

an
can
man
ran
had
dad

1. The _____ was on the bike.

2. He _____ a bag of apples.

3. He waved to my _____.

4. Then _____ apple fell.

5. My dad _____.

6. My dad _____ help.

TEKS 1.22C Spell high-frequency words from a commonly used list.

1. am
2. at
3. cat
4. hat
5. has
6. and

A. Write the spelling words that begin like **apple**.

1. _____

2. _____

3. _____

B. Write the spelling words that have **short a** in the middle, like **bat**.

4. _____

5. _____

6. _____

School Home This unit targets the **short a** sound. Ask your child to read the spelling words aloud.

TEKS 1.22A Use phonological knowledge to match sounds to letters to construct known words. **1.22C** Spell high-frequency words from a commonly used list.

47

A. Write the words that have two sounds.

1. _____

2. _____

B. Write the words that have three sounds.

3. _____

4. _____

5. _____

6. _____

am
at
cat
hat
has
and

C. Use your pencil to track the letters in a-b-c order.
The first two are tracked for you.

f (a) g (b) w r c l s d v e f
a b g t h d q i n j h k l
m z c n d o i x p d q r w
s g t o m u b s v w h x l
y v z

TEKS 1.22A Use phonological knowledge to match sounds to letters to construct known words. **1.22Bi** Use letter-sound patterns to spell: consonant-vowel-consonant (CVC) words. **1.22C** Spell high-frequency words from a commonly used list.

Write the correct word in each sentence.

has   cat

1. The _____ ran up a tree.

2. The man _____ a hammer.

am   and

3. I _____ happy.

4. I can run _____ jump.

at   hat

5. The monkey had on a tan _____.

6. Jan is _____ school.

am
at
cat
hat
has
and

TEKS 1.22C Spell high-frequency words from a commonly used list.

Cat-astrophe

Cat is fat.   Hat went splat.
When he sat   That was that!
On my hat,   — Kevin O'Hara

Write another poem about the cat. Use spelling words.

_____

I _____ not fat.

I am just a big _____.

I sat on that _____,

_____

_____ I made it flat

to get _____ the rat

he _____ under his hat.

am
at
cat
hat
has
and

50

1. let
2. get
3. net
4. pet
5. pen
6. men

A. Write the spelling words that end with **en**.

1. _____

2. _____

B. Write the spelling words that end with **et**.

3. _____

4. _____

5. _____

6. _____

 School Home This unit teaches **short e**. Ask your child to find the rhyming words on the spelling list.

TEKS 1.22Bi Use letter-sound patterns to spell: consonant-vowel-consonant (CVC) words. 1.22C Spell high-frequency words from a commonly used list.

51

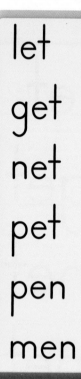

let

get

net

pet

pen

men

A. Four spelling words rhyme. Write the words.
Circle the letters that are the same in all the words.

1. _____   2. _____

_____   _____

3. _____   4. _____

_____   _____

B. Write the word that rhymes and tells about the picture.

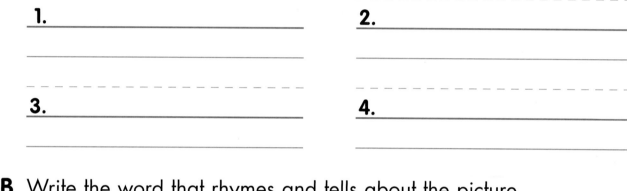

5. ten __?__   6. hen __?__

_____   _____

7. wet __?__   8. get __?__

_____   _____

TEKS 1.22A Use phonological knowledge to match sounds to letters to construct known words. **1.22C** Spell high-frequency words from a commonly used list.

Write a spelling word to complete each sentence.

men	pen

let
get
net
pet
pen
men

1. Sam has a red _____ .

2. The _____ ran on the sand.

let	pet	get	net

3. The _____ has a hole in it.

4. Pam can _____ a fan.

5. Ben has a _____ dog.

6. Dan _____ the cat in.

TEKS 1.22C Spell high-frequency words from a commonly used list.

Write spelling words to complete the story.

let

get

net

pet

pen

men

1. A big snake is in the _____.

2. The snake is a big _____.

3. The girl _____ the snake out.

4. The _____ see the snake.

5. One man tried to _____ the snake.

6. At last he used a _____.

TEKS 1.22C Spell high-frequency words from a commonly used list.

Spelling Words

1. jet
2. set
3. met
4. bed
5. yes
6. leg

A. Write the spelling words that end with **et**.

1. _____

2. _____

3. _____

B. Write a spelling word to name each picture.

4. _____

5. _____

6. _____

School to Home This unit targets the **short e** sound. Ask your child to read the spelling words aloud.

TEKS 1.22C Spell high-frequency words from a commonly used list.

Connections to PHONICS

Write the spelling word that begins with the same sound and letter as the picture name.

1.

_____

- - - - - - - - - - - - - - - - - -

_____

2.

_____

- - - - - - - - - - - - - - - - - -

_____

3.

_____

- - - - - - - - - - - - - - - - - -

_____

4.

_____

- - - - - - - - - - - - - - - - - -

_____

5.

_____

- - - - - - - - - - - - - - - - - -

_____

6.

_____

- - - - - - - - - - - - - - - - - -

_____

TEKS 1.22A Use phonological knowledge to match sounds to letters to construct known words. **1.22C** Spell high-frequency words from a commonly used list.

jet
set
met
bed
yes
leg

A. Write the spelling words that name things.

1. _____

2. _____

3. _____

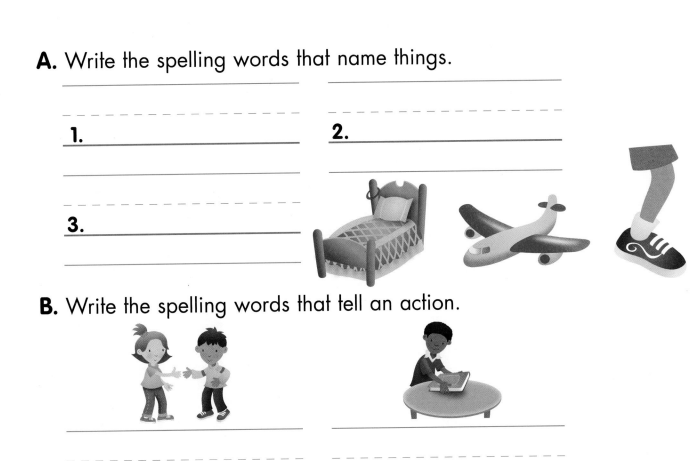

B. Write the spelling words that tell an action.

4. _____

5. _____

C. Write the spelling word that is the opposite of "no."

6. _____

TEKS 1.22C Spell high-frequency words from a commonly used list.

Connections to WRITING

Write a spelling word to finish each tongue twister.

jet
set
met
bed
yes
leg

1. Sue _____ six shells in the shack.

2. Matt _____ merry mice in the mud.

3. Jack jumped on the jolly _____.

4. Lucky laid down on Lil's left _____.

5. _____, the yellow yak yelled, "Yippee!"

6. Bill's _____ has a blue blanket.

TEKS 1.22A Use phonological knowledge to match sounds to letters to construct known words. **1.22C** Spell high-frequency words from a commonly used list.

Review

1. an
2. can
3. man
4. ran
5. had
6. dad

This unit reviews **short a** and **short e**. Ask your child to read the spelling list on each page aloud.

Unit 1: **Short a: VC, CVC**

A. Write the word that begins the same as **apple**.

1. _____

B. Add a letter to **ad** to write words that begin with the same sound as the picture.

2. _____   3. _____

C. Add a letter to **an** to write words that begin with the same sound as the picture.

4. _____   5. _____

6. _____

59

Review

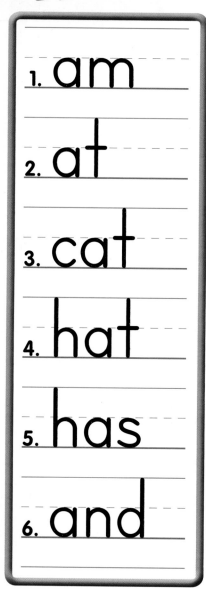

1. am
2. at
3. cat
4. hat
5. has
6. and

Unit 2: **Short a: VC, CVC**

A. Write the spelling words that end with **at**.

1. _____

2. _____

3. _____

B. Write a spelling word to fill each blank.

4. Jack _____ Jill went up the hill.

5. I _____ so smart.

6. Our cat _____ three kittens.

Review

1. let
2. get
3. net
4. pet
5. pen
6. men

Unit 3: **Short e: CVC**

A. Write the spelling word that names the picture.

1. _____

2. _____

3. _____

4. _____

B. Write the words that rhyme with **net** and **pet**. Put a line under the word family **et**.

5. _____

6. _____

Review

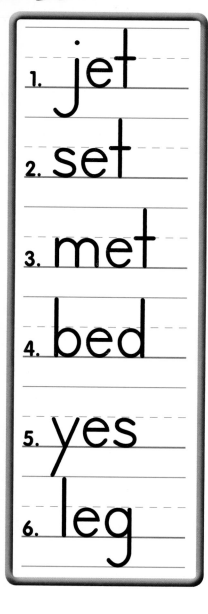

1. jet
2. set
3. met
4. bed
5. yes
6. leg

Unit 4: **Short e: CVC**

A. Write the spelling word to fill in each blank.

1. You sit in a chair. You sleep on a __?__ .

2. Your hand is on your arm.

Your foot is on your __?__ .

1. _____

2. _____

B. Name each picture. Write the first letter of each picture name to make a spelling word.

3. _____

4. _____

5. _____

6. _____

1. it
2. bit
3. sit
4. is
5. his
6. in

A. Write the spelling words that end with **is**.

1. _____

2. _____

B. Write the spelling words that end with **it**.

3. _____

4. _____

5. _____

C. Write the spelling word that ends with **n**.

6. _____

 This unit teaches **short i**. Ask your child to name words that rhyme with **bit**.

TEKS 1.22Bi Use letter-sound patterns to spell: consonant-vowel-consonant (CVC) words. **1.22C** Spell high-frequency words from a commonly used list.

A. Write the spelling words that begin with the same sound.

1. _____

2. _____

3. _____

it
bit
sit
is
his
in

Circle the number of sounds in each word above.

I   2   3

B. Blend the first sound in each picture name to say a spelling word. Write the word.

4. _____ 5. _____

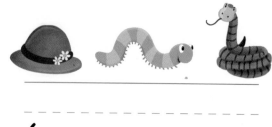

6. _____

TEKS 1.22A Use phonological knowledge to match sounds to letters to construct known words.
1.22C Spell high-frequency words from a commonly used list.

Write a spelling word to complete each sentence.

| it |
| bit |
| sit |
| is |
| his |
| in |

1. Marcus _____ the apple.

2. Sam's hat _____ big.

3. Han has a new cat. He likes _____.

4. Will you _____ in this chair?

5. Dad can sit _____ the sun.

6. Li has a book in _____ bag.

TEKS 1.22C Spell high-frequency words from a commonly used list.

65

Look at the pictures. Write the spelling words to finish the story.

The Dog and His Bone

it
bit
sit
is
his
in

1. The dog _____ the bone.

2. See the dog _____ in front of the window.

3. He sees a dog that wants _____ bone.

4. He drops his bone _____ the street.

5. The dog _____ sad.

6. The dog wishes he did not drop _____.

TEKS 1.22C Spell high-frequency words from a commonly used list.

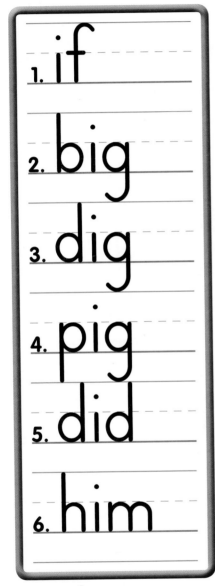

1. if
2. big
3. dig
4. pig
5. did
6. him

A. Write the spelling word that begins with the same sound as the picture name.

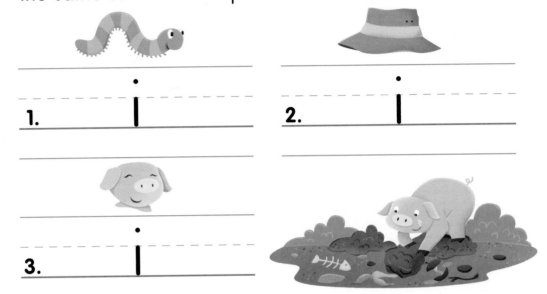

1. i

2. i

3. i

B. Start with **pig**. Change one letter. Write the new word.

p to **b**

4. i

b to **d**

5. i

g to **d**

6. i

School Home

This unit targets the **short i** sound. Ask your child to read the spelling words to you.

TEKS 1.22A Use phonological knowledge to match sounds to letters to construct known words. **1.22Bi** Use letter-sound patterns to spell: consonant-vowel-consonant (CVC) words. **1.22C** Spell high-frequency words from a commonly used list.

Write the word that rhymes with the underlined word and goes with the picture.

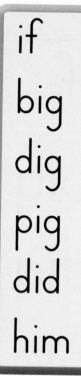

if
big
dig
pig
did
him

1. Bev has a <u>dig</u>.

_____

_____

2. Dad's hand is <u>pig</u>.

_____

_____

3. I <u>hid</u> get a pet.

_____

_____

4. The cat ran to <u>dim</u>.

_____

_____

5. The men will <u>big</u> a hole.

_____

_____

6. Get the hat <u>stiff</u> you can.

_____

_____

TEKS 1.22A Use phonological knowledge to match sounds to letters to construct known words. **1.22Bi** Use letter-sound patterns to spell: consonant-vowel-consonant (CVC) words. **1.22C** Spell high-frequency words from a commonly used list.

Write each spelling word once to complete the story.

   Once there was a pink __1.__ named Squeak.
He loved to __2.__ in his pen.
   Squeak saw a garden full of vegetables.
   Squeak said, "I want to eat those vegetables.
Maybe __3.__ I dig a __4.__ hole I will get to the garden."
And he __5.__! Squeak ate and ate.
   "Get __6.__!" shouted the farmer. "Get him out of my garden!"
   Squeak ran to his pen and hid. He never tried to dig out of the
pen again!

if
big
dig
pig
did
him

1. _____

2. _____

3. _____

4. _____

5. _____

6. _____

TEKS 1.22C Spell high-frequency words from a commonly used list.

69

Connections to WRITING

Write the spelling words to finish the story.

_____

1. The _____ wolf yelled.

2. "Little _____ , let me in!"

3. "I will break down your door _____ you do not

   let me in," the wolf said.

4. "I will not let you in!" said the pig to _____ .

5. The wolf _____ break the door.

6. The pig said, "I will run and _____ a hole."

Tell what happens to the wolf.

if
big
dig
pig
did
him

TEKS 1.22C Spell high-frequency words from a commonly used list.

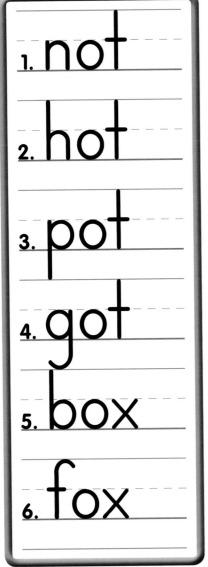

1. not
2. hot
3. pot
4. got
5. box
6. fox

A. Write the spelling words that end in **ox**.

1. _____   2. _____

B. Write the spelling words that end in **ot**.

3. _____   4. _____

5. _____   6. _____

School Home This unit is about **short o**. Ask your child to name other words that rhyme with **hot**.

TEKS 1.22C Spell high-frequency words from a commonly used list.

A. Name the picture. Match the sound you hear at the beginning of the picture to write the first letter of a spelling word. Write **ox** to finish each word.

not	
hot	
pot	
got	
box	
fox	

1.

_____

- - - - - - - - - - -

_____

2.

_____

- - - - - - - - - - -

_____

B. Name each picture. Match the sound you hear at the beginning of each picture to write the first and last letters of each spelling word.

3.

_____

- - - - - - - O - -

_____

4.

_____

- - - - - - - O - -

_____

5.

_____

- - - - - - - O - -

_____

6.

_____

- - - - - - - O - -

_____

TEKS 1.22A Use phonological knowledge to match sounds to letters to construct known words. **1.22Bi** Use letter-sound patterns to spell: consonant-vowel-consonant (CVC) words. **1.22C** Spell high-frequency words from a commonly used list.

Connections to READING

A. Write the spelling word that means the opposite.

1. cold

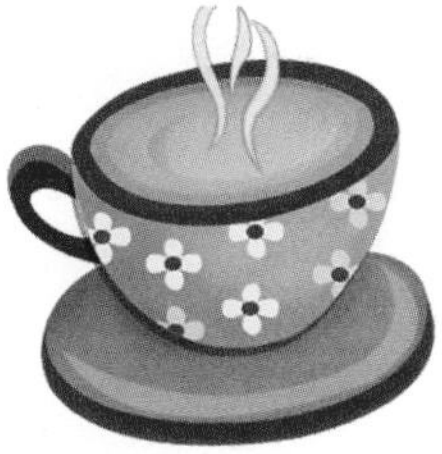

B. Write the spelling word that goes with each pair of words.

2. bird, deer,

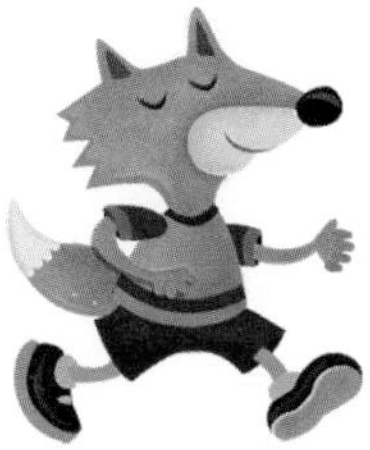

3. pan, dish,

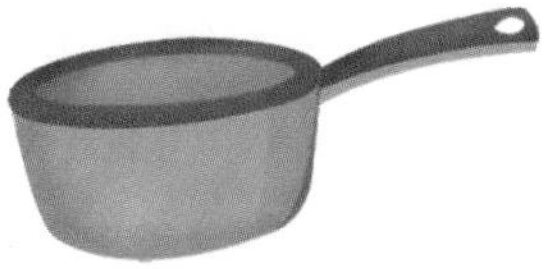

4. get, gave,

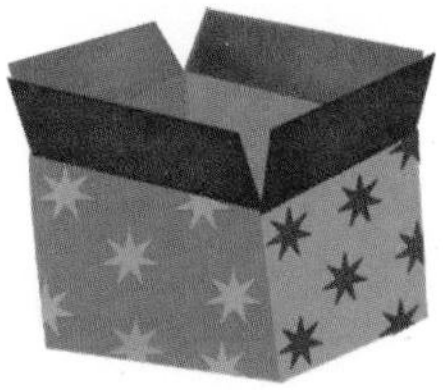

5. no, never,

6. bag, sack,

not
hot
pot
got
box
fox

TEKS 1.22C Spell high-frequency words from a commonly used list.

Write a spelling word to complete each sentence. Then tell what will happen next.

not

hot

pot

got

box

fox

1. The crow has cheese. The _____ wants it.

2. The crow will _____ give the cheese to the fox.

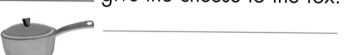

3. "I will make cheese soup for us in a big _____," the fox said.

4. "Will the soup be good and _____?" asked the crow.

5. "Yes," the fox said. "Put the cheese in this _____."

6. The fox _____ the cheese in the box.

TEKS 1.22C Spell high-frequency words from a commonly used list.

Spelling List

1. on
2. mom
3. job
4. hop
5. top
6. mop

A. Write the spelling words that end in **op**.

1. _____

2. _____

3. _____

B. Write the spelling word that has the same first and last letter.

4. _____

C. Write the word that has two letters.

5. _____

D. Write the word that begins with the same sound as **jet**.

6. _____

School Home
This unit teaches **short o**. Help your child read the words in the spelling list aloud.

TEKS **1.22A** Use phonological knowledge to match sounds to letters to construct known words. **1.22C** Spell high-frequency words from a commonly used list.

Name each picture. Then say the beginning sound of each picture name. Write the word you say.

on
mom
job
hop
top
mop

1.

_____

- - - - - - - - - - - -

_____

2.

_____

- - - - - - - - - - - -

_____

3.

_____

- - - - - - - - - - - -

_____

4.

_____

- - - - - - - - - - - -

_____

5.

_____

- - - - - - - - - - - -

_____

6.

_____

- - - - - - - - - - - -

_____

TEKS 1.22A Use phonological knowledge to match sounds to letters to construct known words. **1.22C** Spell high-frequency words from a commonly used list.

Connections to READING

A. Write the spelling word that is the opposite.

1. off ______

2. bottom ______

B. Write the word that tells what someone is doing.

3. 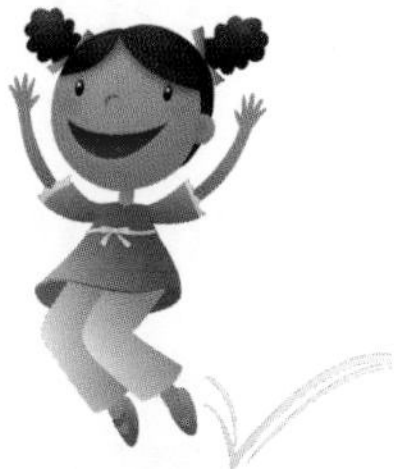 ______

4. 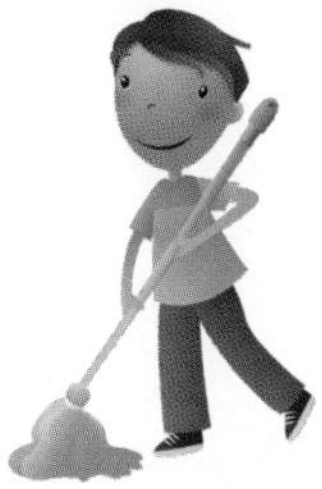 ______

5–6. 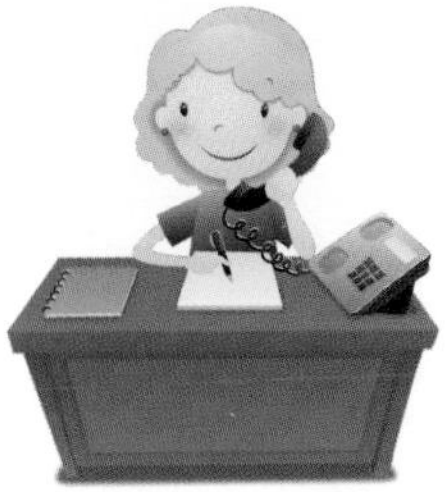 My ______ has a big ______.

on
mom
job
hop
top
mop

TEKS 1.22C Spell high-frequency words from a commonly used list.

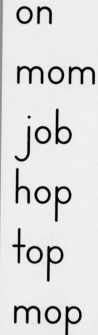

Connections to WRITING

Write spelling words to finish the story.

Word Box: on, mom, job, hop, top, mop

1. I get _____ the stool.

2. I want the drink on _____ of the table.

3. I _____ down off the stool.

4. My _____ sees me drop the drink.

5. She has a _____ for me.

6. I get to _____ the floor.

Circle **yes** or **no**.

Has this happened to you?   yes   no

Did you help mop the floor?   yes   no

TEKS 1.22C Spell high-frequency words from a commonly used list.

1. it

2. bit

3. sit

4. is

5. his

6. in

Unit 6: **Short i: VC, CVC**

Write two spelling words to finish each sentence.

1–2. This book _____

_____

_____ .

3–4. I will _____

_____

_____ this chair.

5–6. Ow! _____

_____

_____ me!

School Home This unit reviews **short i** and **short o**. Ask your child to read the spelling words on each page aloud.

Review

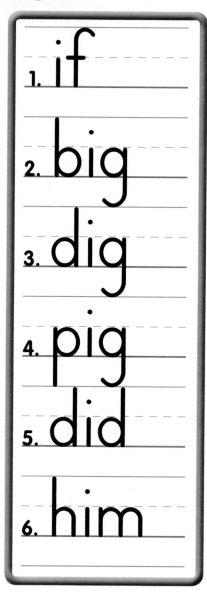

1. if
2. big
3. dig
4. pig
5. did
6. him

Unit 7: Short i: VC, CVC

A. Write the spelling words that end with **ig**.

1. _____

2. _____

3. _____

B. Write the word that has the same first and last letter.

4. _____

C. Write the word that has two letters.

5. _____

D. Write the word that starts with the same sound as

6. _____

Review

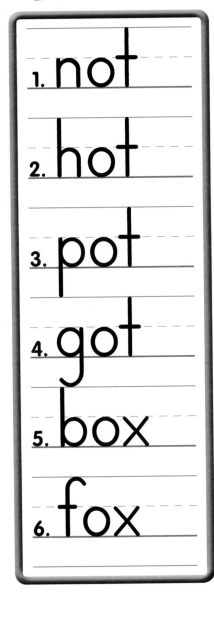

1. not
2. hot
3. pot
4. got
5. box
6. fox

Unit 8: Short o: VC, CVC

A. Add a letter to **ox** to make two words.

FRAGILE

1. _____   2. _____

B. Add a letter to **ot** to make four words.

3. _____   4. _____

5. _____   6. _____

Review

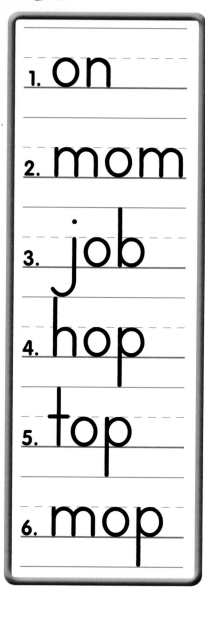

1. on
2. mom
3. job
4. hop
5. top
6. mop

Unit 9: **Short o: VC, CVC**

A. Write the words that end with **op**.

1. _____

2. _____

3. _____

B. Write a spelling word to answer each question.

4. Which word is the same backward and forward?

5. Which word is **no** spelled backward?

6. Which word starts with the same sound as ___?

up
1.

us
2.

bus
3.

cut
4.

but
5.

nut
6.

A. Write the spelling words that end in **us**.

1. _____   2. _____

B. Write the spelling words that end in **ut**.

3. _____   4. _____

5. _____

C. Write the spelling word that ends in **up**.

6. _____

This unit teaches **short u**. Ask your child to name other words that start with **short u** as in **up**.

 TEKS 1.22C Spell high-frequency words from a commonly used list.

Write the spelling words that begin with the same sound as the picture names.

up
us
bus
cut
but
nut

1. _____

2. _____

3. _____

4. _____

5. _____

6. _____

TEKS 1.22A Use phonological knowledge to match sounds to letters to construct known words.
1.22C Spell high-frequency words from a commonly used list.

Write a spelling word to finish each sentence.
Circle **yes** if the sentence tells about the picture.
Circle **no** if it does not tell about the picture.

up
us
bus
cut
but
nut

1. The bird is _____ in the sky.   yes   no

2. Jan gets on the _____ .   yes   no

3. The _____ is in the box.   yes   no

4. My dog runs to _____ .   yes   no

5. Mom will _____ the big apple.   yes   no

6. The day was cold, _____ now it is hot.   yes   no

TEKS 1.22C Spell high-frequency words from a commonly used list.

85

A. Write a spelling word to complete each sentence.

A __1.__ trip is fun. You go __2.__ the steps. You find a good seat. Take a snack with you. You can __3.__ an apple and a carrot. Put in a __4.__ or two. Eat on the bus, __5.__ save some for __6.__ .

up

us

bus

cut

but

nut

1. _____

2. _____

3. _____

4. _____

5. _____

6. _____

B. Write about a bus trip. Tell what you want to see. Use spelling words.

_____

I want to see _____

_____

_____

TEKS 1.22C Spell high-frequency words from a commonly used list.

1. fun
2. run
3. sun
4. tug
5. bug
6. rug

A. Write the spelling words that end in **ug**.

1. _____

2. _____

3. _____

B. Write the spelling words that end in **un**.

4. _____

5. _____

6. _____

 **School Home**
This unit teaches **short u**. Ask your child to identify the rhyming words on the list.

TEKS 1.22C Spell high-frequency words from a commonly used list.

Replace the middle letter in each word to write a spelling word.

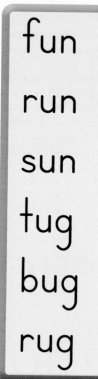

fun

run

sun

tug

bug

rug

big

1. _____

fan

2. _____

rag

3. _____

ran

4. _____

son

5. _____

tag

6. _____

TEKS 1.22C Spell high-frequency words from a commonly used list.

Write the spelling word that matches each meaning.

fun
run
sun
tug
bug
rug

1. This word means "a good time."

_____

- - - - - - - - - - - - - - - - - -

_____

2. It is another name for an insect.

_____

- - - - - - - - - - - - - - - - - -

_____

3. This is a covering for a floor.

_____

- - - - - - - - - - - - - - - - - -

_____

4. You do this when you pull on something.

_____

- - - - - - - - - - - - - - - - - -

_____

5. It gives us heat and light.

_____

- - - - - - - - - - - - - - - - - -

_____

6. This means "to move very fast on foot."

_____

- - - - - - - - - - - - - - - - - -

_____

TEKS 1.22C Spell high-frequency words from a commonly used list.

89

A. Write a spelling word to complete each sentence.

fun
run
sun
tug
bug
rug

We play in the warm __1.__ on a summer day. We __2.__ a race. We pull and __3.__ on a rope. We see a yellow __4.__ on a leaf. We sit on a __5.__ to eat. We laugh and have lots of __6.__ !

1. _____

2. _____

3. _____

4. _____

5. _____

6. _____

B. Write about a summer day. Tell what you do. Use spelling words.

On a summer day I _____

TEKS 1.22C Spell high-frequency words from a commonly used list.

1. bad
2. yet
3. fix
4. dot
5. hug
6. tub

A. Write letters to finish each spelling word.

1. a

2. i

3. o

4. e

B. Write a **u** to finish each spelling word.

5. h   g

6. t   b

This unit reviews the **short vowel sounds**. Ask your child to name a word that rhymes with each spelling word.

 TEKS 1.22Bi Use letter-sound patterns to spell: consonant-vowel-consonant (CVC) words. **1.22C** Spell high-frequency words from a commonly used list.

91

Name each picture. Match the sound you hear at the beginning, middle, and end of the picture names to write a spelling word.

| bad |
| yet |
| fix |
| dot |
| hug |
| tub |

1.

_____

2.

_____

3.

_____

4.

_____

5.

_____

6.

_____

92

TEKS 1.22A Use phonological knowledge to match sounds to letters to construct known words. 1.22Bi Use letter-sound patterns to spell: consonant-vowel-consonant (CVC) words. 1.22C Spell high-frequency words from a commonly used list.

Connections to READING

Write the spelling word that completes each sentence.

1. Can I ___?___ the net?

2. Is the ___?___ red?

3. The cat was ___?___ .

4. You can ___?___ Mom.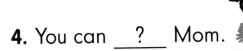

5. Can pup get in the ___?___ ?

6. Can you see the sun rise ___?___ ?

| bad |
| yet |
| fix |
| dot |
| hug |
| tub |

TEKS 1.22C Spell high-frequency words from a commonly used list.

A. Write spelling words to finish the letter.

Dear Grandma,

My new pup has a black __1.__ on his head. He was __2.__ today. He ran in the mud. I had to wash him in the __3.__. We had to __4.__ the fence, too. He does not know how to sit __5.__. He does like to __6.__ me.

Love, Fran

bad
yet
fix
dot
hug
tub

1. _____

2. _____

3. _____

4. _____

5. _____

6. _____

B. Write a letter on a sheet of paper. Tell about your day. Use spelling words.

TEKS 1.22C Spell high-frequency words from a commonly used list.

1. a
2. I
3. to
4. of
5. the
6. was
7. are

A. Write the two spelling words that have only one letter.

1. _____

2. _____

B. Write the spelling word that sounds like the name of the letter **r**.

3. _____

C. Write the spelling word that begins with the same sound as the picture name.

4. _____

D. Name each picture. Match the sound you hear at the beginning of the picture name to the sound you hear at the end of a spelling word. Write the word.

5. _____

6. _____

E. Write the spelling word that begins with two letters that make one sound.

7. _____

School Home

This unit teaches **commonly used writing words**. Help your child practice writing each word on the spelling list.

 TEKS 1.22A Use phonological knowledge to match sounds to letters to construct known words. **1.22C** Spell high-frequency words from a commonly used list.

Use the clues to find the spelling words. Write the words.

1. ● one letter ■ a capital letter
   ▲ sounds like its name

   _____

   - - - - - - - - - - - - - - - - -

   _____

2. ● three letters ■ two sounds
   ▲ the **e** makes no sound

   _____

   - - - - - - - - - - - - - - - - -

   _____

3. ● three letters ■ two sounds
   ▲ the **e** makes a sound

   _____

   - - - - - - - - - - - - - - - - -

   _____

4. ● three letters ■ three sounds
   ▲ starts like **win**

   _____

   _____

5. ● one letter ■ one sound
   ▲ sometimes sounds like
   its letter name

   _____

   - - - - - - - - - - - - - - - - -

   _____

6. ● two letters ■ two sounds
   ▲ starts like **tug**

   _____

   _____

7. ● two letters ■ two sounds
   ▲ ends with the **v** sound

   _____

   - - - - - - - - - - - - - - - - -

   _____

a
I
to
of
the
was
are

TEKS 1.22A Use phonological knowledge to match sounds to letters to construct known words. **1.22C** Spell high-frequency words from a commonly used list.

A. Write the spelling words that go before words that name things.

1. _____   2. _____

B. Write the spelling word you use to tell about you.

3. _____

C. Write a spelling word to finish each sentence.

to	was	are	of

4. The men _____ wet.

5. Pam _____ on a jet.

6. Jim ran _____ the bed.

7. Ed has one _____ the pens.

a
I
to
of
the
was
are

TEKS 1.22C Spell high-frequency words from a commonly used list.

Connections to WRITING

A. Write a spelling word to finish each line of the poem.

Last night _____ dreamed I _____ a star,

And I was shining where you _____ .

Full _____ blinking, twinkling light,

I could brighten up _____ night.

I sent _____ happy light _____ you

So you could dream some sweet dreams, too.

B. Write a poem about something you would like to be. Use spelling words.

a
I
to
of
the
was
are

TEKS 1.22C Spell high-frequency words from a commonly used list. **1.22E** Use resources to find correct spellings.

Review

1. up
2. us
3. bus
4. cut
5. but
6. nut

This unit reviews **short u**, short vowels, and commonly used words. Ask your child to read the spelling words on each page aloud.

Unit 11: **Short u: VC, CVC**

A. Change the vowel in the middle to write a spelling word.

cat

net

1. _____

2. _____

bit

3. _____

B. Write the spelling word that rhymes.

fuss

cup

4. _____

5. _____

C. Change the first letter to write a spelling word.

is

6. _____

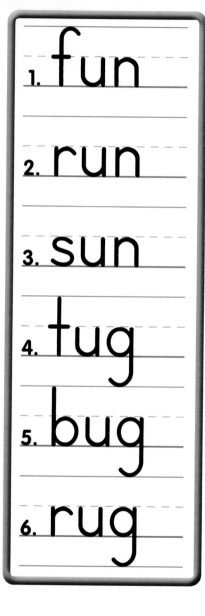

1. fun
2. run
3. sun
4. tug
5. bug
6. rug

Unit 12: Short u: CVC

Name each picture. Match the sound you hear at the beginning, middle, and end of each picture name to write a spelling word.

1. _____

2. _____

3. _____

4. _____

5. _____

6. _____

Review

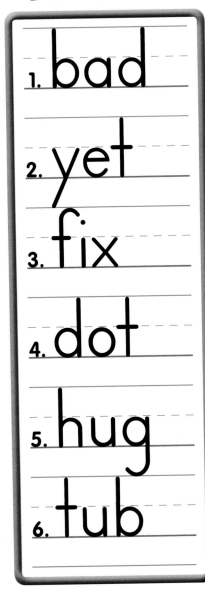

1. bad
2. yet
3. fix
4. dot
5. hug
6. tub

Unit 13: Short Vowel Review: CVC

Write the spelling word that begins with the same sound as each picture name.

1. ___ o ___

2. ___ u ___

3. ___ i ___

4. ___ e ___

5. ___ a ___

6. ___ u ___

Review

1. a
2. I
3. to
4. of
5. the
6. was
7. are

Unit 14: Words Writers Use

Use the clues to write each spelling word.

1. ends with **f** that sounds like a **v**

2. starts with two letters that make one sound

3. ends with **s** that sounds like a **z**

4. has an **e** that makes no sound

5. a capital letter that sounds like its name

6. one letter and sometimes sounds like its name

7. starts with the same sound as **top**

1. grin
2. spin
3. skip
4. frog
5. plum
6. slam

A. Write the spelling words that begin with a consonant and **r**.

1. _____   2. _____

B. Write the spelling words that begin with a consonant and **l**.

3. _____   4. _____

C. Write the spelling words that begin with **sp** and **sk**.

5. _____   6. _____

This unit teaches consonant blends, such as **gr** in **grin**. Help your child name other words that start with these blends.

TEKS 1.22Biii Use letter-sound patterns to spell: one-syllable words with consonant blends. **1.22C** Spell high-frequency words from a commonly used list.

Name each picture. Match the sound you hear at the beginning of each picture name to the two letters that begin a spelling word. Write the word.

grin
spin
skip
frog
plum
slam

1.

_____

- - - - - - - - - - -

_____

2.

_____

- - - - - - - - - - -

_____

3.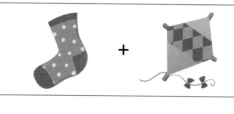

_____

- - - - - - - - - - -

_____

4.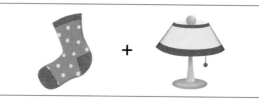

_____

- - - - - - - - - - -

_____

5.

_____

- - - - - - - - - - -

_____

6.

_____

- - - - - - - - - - -

_____

TEKS 1.22A Use phonological knowledge to match sounds to letters to construct known words. **1.22Biii** Use letter-sound patterns to spell: one-syllable words with consonant blends. **1.22C** Spell high-frequency words from a commonly used list.

Write a spelling word to finish each sentence.

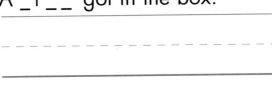

1. I can run and _ _ _ p.

2. A _ r _ _ got in the box.

3. Dad had a big g _ _ _ !

4. I can _ _ i _ a top.

5. Ron has a big p _ _ _.

6. I will not _ _ a _ the door.

grin

spin

skip

frog

plum

slam

TEKS 1.22C Spell high-frequency words from a commonly used list.

105

A. Write spelling words to finish the story.

The ___**1.**___ looks up. He sees a big ___**2.**___ . The frog goes up the tree. He tries to ___**3.**___ the plum to snap the stem. Oh, no! The plum falls. It will ___**4.**___ on the ground. It will bounce and ___**5.**___ into the pond. The frog is not sad. He has a big ___**6.**___ .

1. _____	**2.** _____
3. _____	**4.** _____
5. _____	**6.** _____

grin
spin
skip
frog
plum
slam

B. Write about the story.

Do you think the frog will get the plum? _____

Why? _____

_____

TEKS 1.22C Spell high-frequency words from a commonly used list.

1. best
2. rest
3. fast
4. must
5. step
6. still

A. Write the spelling words that begin with **st**.

1. _____

2. _____

B. Write the spelling words that end in **st**.

3. _____

4. _____

5. _____

6. _____

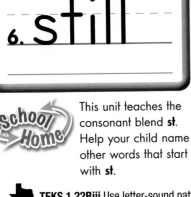

This unit teaches the
consonant blend **st**.
Help your child name
other words that start
with **st**.

TEKS **1.22Biii** Use letter-sound patterns to spell: one-syllable words with consonant blends. **1.22C** Spell high-frequency words from a commonly used list.

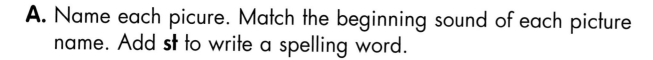

A. Name each picure. Match the beginning sound of each picture name. Add **st** to write a spelling word.

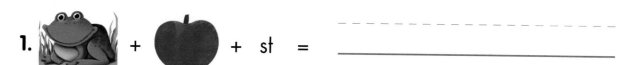

best
rest
fast
must
step
still

1. 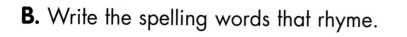 + 🍎 + st = _____

2. 🐭 + ☂ + st = _____

B. Write the spelling words that rhyme.

3. _____

4. _____

C. Put **st** in place of the first letter in each word. Write the spelling word.

dill

5. _____

pep

6. _____

TEKS 1.22A Use phonological knowledge to match sounds to letters to construct known words. **1.22Biii** Use letter-sound patterns to spell: one-syllable words with consonant blends. **1.22C** Spell high-frequency words from a commonly used list.

Complete the spelling words to finish the story.

best
rest
fast
must
step
still

Jen is in a _____ race. Without taking one

__s_____, she can __s_____

have fun. Jen can go __f_____!

Jen __m_____ not __r_____

until the _____ race is over. The __b_____

racer will win a gold cup.

TEKS 1.22C Spell high-frequency words from a commonly used list.

109

Connections to WRITING

A. Write spelling words to finish the story.

Once, the Pony Express was the ___**1.**___ way to get mail to the West. A rider on a ___**2.**___ horse took mail bags many miles. He did not ___**3.**___ until he got the mail to another horse and rider. The new horse and rider did not miss a ___**4.**___. The rider knew he ___**5.**___ hurry. He could ___**6.**___ ride fast after many hours.

best	
rest	
fast	
must	
step	
still	

1. _____

2. _____

3. _____

4. _____

5. _____

6. _____

B. Would this be a good way to send mail today? Why or why not? Write what you think.

_____

_____

_____

TEKS 1.22C Spell high-frequency words from a commonly used list.

1. bugs

2. cats

3. pigs

4. sits

5. runs

6. gets

A. Add and write.

1. I 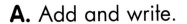 + I ____ = 2 _____

2. I ____ + I ____ = 2 _____

3. I ____ + I ____ = 2 _____

B. Add **s** to each word. Write the spelling word.

4. get _____

5. run _____

6. sit _____

TEKS **1.22C** Spell high-frequency words from a commonly used list. **1.22D** Spell base words with inflectional endings.

Connections to PHONICS

A. Change each vowel sound to say a spelling word. Write the word.

1. cots _____

2. sets _____

3. bags _____

4. pegs _____

| bugs |
| cats |
| pigs |
| sits |
| runs |
| gets |

B. Sometimes when you add **s,** it makes the sound of **s.** Sometimes it makes the sound of **z.**

5. Write the word that ends with the sound of **z.** _____

6. Write the word that ends with the sound of **s.** _____

112

TEKS 1.22C Spell high-frequency words from a commonly used list. 1.22D Spell base words with inflectional endings.

Look at the picture. Write spelling words to complete the sentences.

bugs

cats

pigs

sits

runs

gets

A frog _____ on a log.

It _____ the _____ .

The _____ dig in the mud. The _____

rest in the sun. A lamb _____ in the grass.

TEKS 1.22C Spell high-frequency words from a commonly used list.

113

A. Write spelling words to finish the story.

Ben lives on a farm. He feeds the ___**1.**___ . He ___**2.**___ eggs from the hens. He pets his two ___**3.**___ . He ___**4.**___ to catch the cow. Then he ___**5.**___ on the hay to rest. He sees some ___**6.**___ .

bugs

cats

pigs

sits

runs

gets

1. _____

2. _____

3. _____

4. _____

5. _____

6. _____

B. What would you like to do on a farm?

_____

_____

_____

TEKS 1.22C Spell high-frequency words from a commonly used list.

Add **ing** to each word in the box.
Write the spelling word.

do	see	keep	feel	go	feed

1. doing

2. going

3. seeing

4. feeding

5. feeling

6. keeping

1. _____

2. _____

3. _____

4. _____

5. _____

6. _____

School Home

This unit focuses on the **-ing** ending. Take turns with your child, saying the spelling words with and without this ending.

TEKS 1.22C Spell high-frequency words from a commonly used list. **1.22D** Spell base words with inflectional endings.

A. Write the words that have the **long e** sound.

1. _____

2. _____

3. _____

4. _____

B. Write the word that has the **long o** sound.

5. _____

C. Write the word that has an **o** that makes a sound like **oo**.

6. _____

doing

going

seeing

feeding

feeling

keeping

TEKS 1.22A Use phonological knowledge to match sounds to letters to construct known words.
1.22C Spell high-frequency words from a commonly used list.

Connections to READING

Write a spelling word to complete each sentence.

1. What is she _____ ?

2. She is _____ the horse's leg.

3. She is _____ if it is hurt.

4. She is _____ to fix the leg.

5. Matt is _____ the horse still.

6. He is _____ it grass.

doing
going
seeing
feeding
feeling
keeping

TEKS 1.22C Spell high-frequency words from a commonly used list.

A. Write spelling words to finish the poem.

My eyes are for   **1.**   .
My fingers are for   **2.**   .
My body is for   **3.**   .
My legs are for   **4.**   .
My mouth is for   **5.**   .
My heart is for   **6.**   .

doing

going

seeing

feeding

feeling

keeping

1. _____

2. _____

3. _____

4. _____

5. _____

6. _____

B. Write a short poem that tells what you see outside in the summer. Tell how you feel. Circle two words you are not sure about. Check the spelling in your dictionary.

TEKS 1.22C Spell high-frequency words from a commonly used list. **1.22E** Use resources to find correct spellings.

Review

1. grin
2. spin
3. skip
4. frog
5. plum
6. slam

Unit 16: Initial Consonant Blends

A. Write the spelling words that begin with an **r** blend.

1. _____

2. _____

B. Write the spelling words that begin with an **l** blend.

3. _____

4. _____

C. Write the spelling word that rhymes with each word.

hip

tin

5. _____

6. _____

This unit reviews consonant blends and the word endings **-s** and **-ing**. Ask your child to read the spelling words on each page aloud.

Review

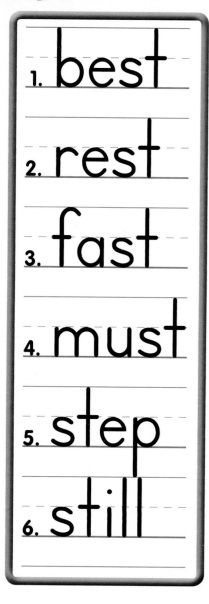

1. best
2. rest
3. fast
4. must
5. step
6. still

Unit 17: **Consonant Blends: st**

A. Complete each spelling word.

1. _____ st

2. _____ st

3. _____ st

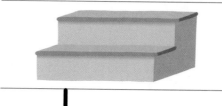

4. st_____

B. Write the spelling word that rhymes with each word.

dust

5. _____

hill

6. _____

Review

1. bugs
2. cats
3. pigs
4. sits
5. runs
6. gets

Unit 18: Inflectional Endings: -s

A. Add **s** to the word to show more than one.

bug

cat

1. _____

2. _____

pig

3. _____

B. Write a spelling word to finish each sentence.

4. One bug _____ on a leaf.

5. One cat _____ in the house.

6. One pig _____ lunch.

Review

1. doing
2. going
3. seeing
4. feeding
5. feeling
6. keeping

Unit 19: Inflectional Endings: -ing

A. Add **ing** to each word to write a spelling word.

1. feel _____

2. keep _____

3. go _____

4. do _____

B. Write the spelling word that goes with each picture.

5. _____

6. _____

1. came

2. name

3. same

4. game

5. gate

6. gave

Use the letter clues to write the spelling words.

1. n _ m _

2. s _ m _

3. g _ m _

4. c _ m _

5. g _ t _

6. g _ v _

 This unit targets the **long a** sound spelled **a-consonant-e**. Ask your child to name rhyming words in the spelling list.

 TEKS 1.22A Use phonological knowledge to match sounds to letters to construct known words. **1.22Bii** Use letter-sound patterns to spell: consonant-vowel-consonant-silent e (CVCe) words. **1.22C** Spell high-frequency words from a commonly used list.

A. Circle the word that has the **long a** sound.
Then write the word you circled.

1.   came   cat

_____

- - - - - - - - - - - -

_____

2.   bad   game

_____

- - - - - - - - - - - -

_____

3.   same   man

_____

- - - - - - - - - - - -

_____

4.   name   nap

_____

- - - - - - - - - - - -

_____

came
name
same
game
gate
gave

B. Write a spelling word that rhymes with each word.

5. cave

_____

- - - - - - - - - - - -

_____

6. late

_____

- - - - - - - - - - - -

_____

124

TEKS 1.22A Use phonological knowledge to match sounds to letters to construct known words.
1.22Bii Use letter-sound patterns to spell: consonant-vowel-consonant-silent e (CVCe) words.
1.22C Spell high-frequency words from a commonly used list.

Connections to READING

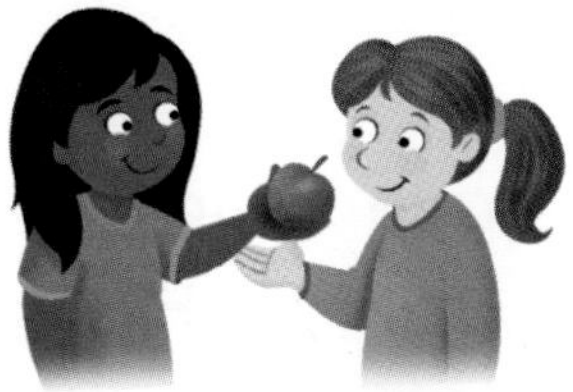

came
name
same
game
gate
gave

Write a spelling word to complete each sentence.

1. I ________________ Kate a big plum.

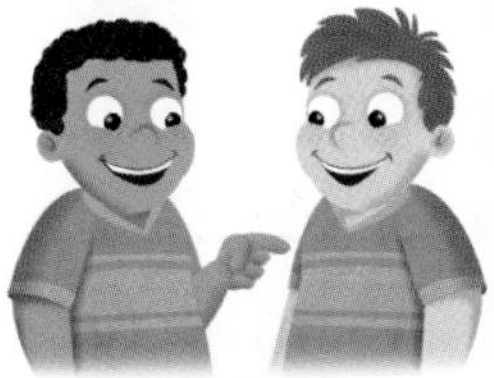

2. Dave and I have the ________________ shirt.

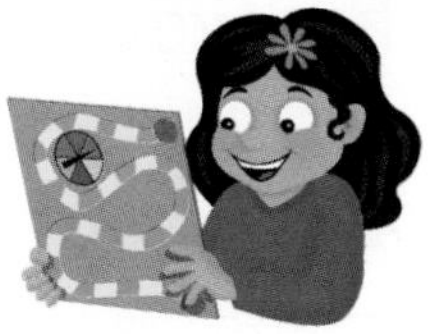

3. Kay has a new ________________ to play.

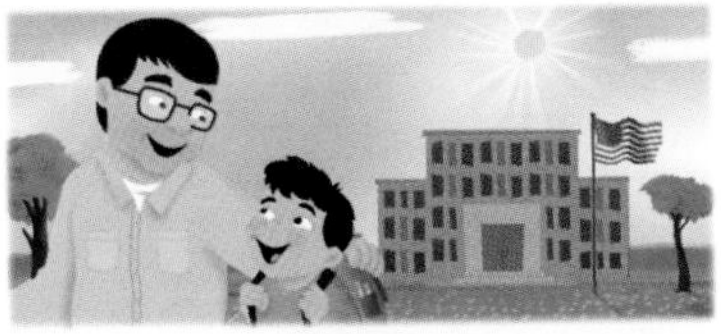

4. My dad ________________ to get me.

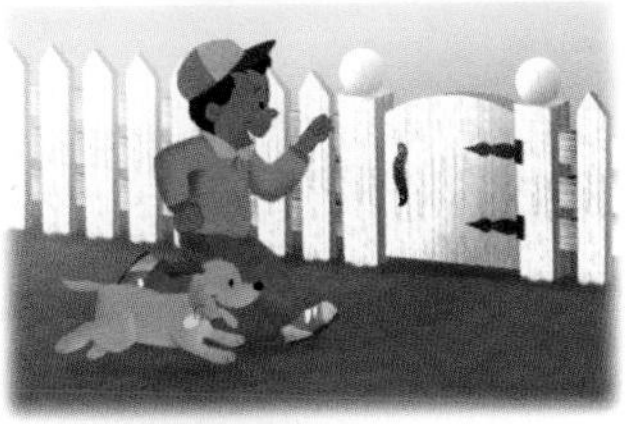

5. Jack ran to open the ________________.

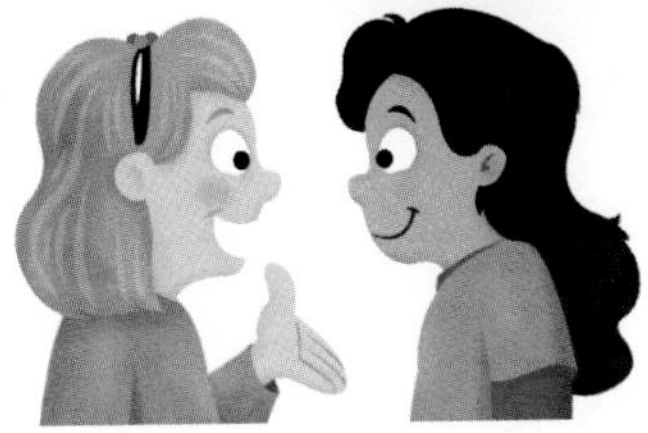

6. What is your ________________?

TEKS 1.22C Spell high-frequency words from a commonly used list.

A. Underline the spelling words you read in the paragraph.

Mom and Dad gave their first baby the same name as Gramps. His is Raymond. I am Raylene. Gramps wrote Ray on the front gate. When I came in, Gramps asked, "Who is Ray?" I said, "I am Ray." He said, "No, I am Ray." Then we said, "We are Ray!" That was a fun game.

came
name
same
game
gate
gave

B. Write each spelling word. Circle the words that rhyme.

1. _____

2. _____

3. _____

4. _____

5. _____

6. _____

C. Use spelling words to write about your name on a separate sheet of paper.

TEKS 1.22C Spell high-frequency words from a commonly used list.

1. lake
2. rake
3. bake
4. make
5. take
6. made

Use the letter clues to write the spelling words.

1. b _ k _

2. l _ k _

3. t _ k _

4. m _ d _

5. r _ k _

6. m _ k _

School Home

This unit targets the **long a** sound spelled **a-consonant-e**. Help your child read the spelling words aloud.

TEKS 1.22A Use phonological knowledge to match sounds to letters to construct known words. **1.22Bii** Use letter-sound patterns to spell: consonant-vowel-consonant-silent e (CVCe) words. **1.22C** Spell high-frequency words from a commonly used list.

A. Circle the **long a** words. Then write them.

1. ran   take   man

2. bake   tack   map

3. rat   tap   made

4. ham   make   mat

| lake |
| rake |
| bake |
| make |
| take |
| made |

B. Write the spelling word that names the picture. Add **s** to the end.

5.  +

6.  +

TEKS 1.22A Use phonological knowledge to match sounds to letters to construct known words. **1.22Bii** Use letter-sound patterns to spell: consonant-vowel-consonant-silent e (CVCe) words. **1.22C** Spell high-frequency words from a commonly used list. **1.22D** Spell base words with inflectional endings.

A. Write the spelling word that goes with each group.

 pond    stream

1. _____

 fry   boil

2. _____

 shovel    hoe

3. _____

lake
rake
bake
make
take
made

B. Write the missing spelling words.

4. I will _____ a cake in the oven.

5. I will _____ it to a party.

6. I will say, "I _____ a cake."

TEKS 1.22C Spell high-frequency words from a commonly used list.

A. Underline the spelling words in the paragraph below.

I like to go to a camp by a lake. I learn lots of fun things. I bake cookies. I make mobiles. I take swimming lessons. Last year, I made a campfire. We had to rake the ground first. Then we put sticks in a pile for the fire.

lake
rake
bake
make
take
made

B. Write each spelling word. Circle the words that rhyme.

1. _____

2. _____

3. _____

4. _____

5. _____

6. _____

C. On a separate sheet of paper, use the spelling words to write about something you would like to do at a camp.

TEKS 1.22A Use phonological knowledge to match sounds to letters to construct known words. **1.22C** Spell high-frequency words from a commonly used list.

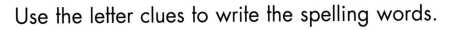

1. he

2. me

3. we

4. she

5. be

6. see

Use the letter clues to write the spelling words.

1. b

2. m

3. sh

4. h

5. s

6. W

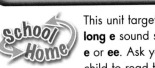
School Home

This unit targets the **long e** sound spelled **e** or **ee**. Ask your child to read the spelling words aloud.

TEKS 1.22A Use phonological knowledge to match sounds to letters to construct known words. **1.22C** Spell high-frequency words from a commonly used list.

A. Use the clue to write the word.

sounds like

has two vowels, has one vowel sound

1. _____

2. _____

begins with two letters that make one sound

3. _____

| he |
| me |
| we |
| she |
| be |
| see |

B. Name the picture. Use the first sound in the picture name and the ending sound in  to make a spelling word. Write the word.

4. _____

5. _____

6. _____

TEKS 1.22A Use phonological knowledge to match sounds to letters to construct known words.
1.22C Spell high-frequency words from a commonly used list.

Write spelling words to finish the rhyme.

Instead of Ann, you can just say __1.__ .
And Ben is sometimes known as __2.__ .
A word for you and me is __3.__ .
Together we're silly as can __4.__ !
When my friends need help they ask __5.__ .
We like each other, as you can __6.__ .

he
me
we
she
be
see

1. _____

2. _____

3. _____

4. _____

5. _____

6. _____

TEKS 1.22A Use phonological knowledge to match sounds to letters to construct known words. **1.22C** Spell high-frequency words from a commonly used list.

A. Underline the spelling words in the paragraph.

   The fox can see the bunny. Then he says, "You can not hide from me."
   The bunny is ready to run. Then she says, "Can we be friends? I have a gift for you. You have to close your eyes."
   The fox wants the gift. The fox shuts his eyes.

| he |
| me |
| we |
| she |
| be |
| see |

B. Write the spelling words.

1. _____

2. _____

3. _____

4. _____

5. _____

6. _____

C. Use the spelling words to write the rest of the story on a separate sheet of paper. How can the bunny get away from the fox?

TEKS 1.22C Spell high-frequency words from a commonly used list.

1. feel
2. deep
3. keep
4. feed
5. seed
6. feet

Write the spelling words that end in **eep**.

1. _____   2. _____

Write the spelling words that end in **eed**.

3. _____   4. _____

Write the spelling word that ends in **l**.

5. _____

Write the spelling word that ends in **t**.

6. _____

This unit targets the **long e** sound spelled **ee**. Ask your child to read each spelling word and circle **ee**.

 TEKS 1.22A Use phonological knowledge to match sounds to letters to construct known words. **1.22C** Spell high-frequency words from a commonly used list.

Write the spelling word that rhymes with each picture.

feel
deep
keep
feed
seed
feet

1. ee

2. ee

3. ee

4. ee

5. ee

6. ee

136

TEKS 1.22A Use phonological knowledge to match sounds to letters to construct known words.
1.22C Spell high-frequency words from a commonly used list.

Write spelling words to complete the paragraph.

Do you want to grow a pumpkin? Start with a pumpkin

__1.__ . Then put dirt in a __2.__ tub. Is the dirt dry?
You can __3.__ it to find out. Seeds need water, so __4.__ the
dirt wet. You can __5.__ the seed with plant food. Soon the
seed will put down roots. The roots are like __6.__ . The plant will stand
on them and grow strong.

| feel |
| deep |
| keep |
| feed |
| seed |
| feet |

1. _____

2. _____

3. _____

4. _____

5. _____

6. _____

TEKS 1.22C Spell high-frequency words from a commonly used list.

A. Underline the spelling words in the paragraph.

   Some people say that a plant has feelings. They dig a deep hole for a seed. They talk to the plant as it grows. They feed the plant. They keep the plant warm. They do not step on the plant with their feet. They want the plant to feel good.

feel
deep
keep
feed
seed
feet

B. Write the spelling words. Draw lines to connect words that rhyme.

1. _____

2. _____

3. _____

4. _____

5. _____

6. _____

C. Do plants have feelings? Use spelling words to write what you think. Check your spelling in a dictionary.

TEKS 1.22C Spell high-frequency words from a commonly used list. **1.22E** Use resources to find correct spellings.

1. came
2. name
3. same
4. game
5. gate
6. gave

This unit reviews **long a** and **long e**. Ask your child to read the spelling words on each page aloud.

Unit 21: Long a: CVCe

A. Fill in each blank to write a different spelling word.

1. __ __ t __ _____

2. __ __ v __ _____

B. Write the words that end with **ame**.

_____   _____

3. _____   4. _____

5. _____   6. _____

Review

1. lake
2. rake
3. bake
4. make
5. take
6. made

Fill in each blank to write a different spelling word.

__ a __ e

1. _____

2. _____

3. _____

4. _____

5. _____

6. _____

Review

1. he
2. me
3. we
4. she
5. be
6. see

Unit 23: Long e: e, ee

Change the vowel. Write a spelling word with **long e**.

hi

1. _____

sea

2. _____

shy

3. _____

wa

4. _____

ma

5. _____

bo

6. _____

Review

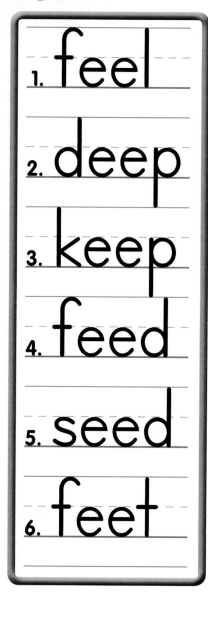

1. feel
2. deep
3. keep
4. feed
5. seed
6. feet

Unit 24: Long e: ee

A. Follow the directions to write the spelling words.

1. Write the word that starts like  and ends like **reed**.

2. Change one letter to make  .

3. Change two letters to make a word that means **touch**.

4. Change one letter to make ____ .

B. Write the words that rhyme with **beep**.

5. _____

6. _____

bite
1.

kite
2.

time
3.

life
4.

line
5.

mine
6.

A. Write the spelling words that end in **ine**.

1. _____

2. _____

B. Write the spelling words that end in **ite**.

3. _____

4. _____

C. Use the letter clue to write a spelling word.

5. _____ f _____

6. _____ m _____

School Home

This unit targets the **long i** sound spelled **i-consonant-e**. Ask your child to name the spelling words that rhyme.

TEKS 1.22Bii Use letter-sound patterns to spell: consonant-vowel-consonant-silent e (CVCe) words. **1.22C** Spell high-frequency words from a commonly used list.

A. Rewrite each word so it will have the **long i** sound.

1. bit

2. mane

3. kit

4. tame

bite
kite
time
life
line
mine

B. Write the words that have the same beginning and middle sounds.

5.

6.

TEKS 1.22A Use phonological knowledge to match sounds to letters to construct known words.
1.22Bii Use letter-sound patterns to spell: consonant-vowel-consonant-silent e (CVCe) words.
1.22C Spell high-frequency words from a commonly used list.

A. Write the spelling word that goes with each group of words.

bite
kite
time
life
line
mine

plane   balloon   **1.** _____

clock   watch   **2.** _____

hers   his   **3.** _____

square   circle   **4.** _____

B. Write a spelling word to finish each sentence.

5. I had the best time of my _____.

6. Did he take a _____ of my sandwich?

TEKS 1.22C Spell high-frequency words from a commonly used list.

Use proofreading marks to fix what you read.
Change a small letter to a capital letter with ≡.
Change a capital letter to a small letter with a /.
Use a ⊙ to add a period.

Proofreading Marks

≡	Capital Letter
/	Small Letter
⊙	Add a Period

bite
kite
time
life
line
mine

A. Underline the spelling words. Then write them on the lines below.

Dear Mike,
I had a good time today⊙My kite flew the highest. I let the line out
all the way. my dog tried to bite it. The first /Prize was mine.
I had never ̲w̲on a prize in my life.

Jake

1. _____

2. _____

3. _____

4. _____

5. _____

6. _____

B. Rewrite the letter. Make the changes shown by the proofreading marks.

C. Write a letter about flying a kite. Try to use all the spelling words.

TEKS 1.22A Use phonological knowledge to match sounds to letters to construct known words. **1.22C** Spell high-frequency words from a commonly used list.

1. bike
2. like
3. hike
4. hide
5. ride
6. side

Finish each spelling word.

1. h__d__

2. r__d__

3. l__k__

4. h__k__

5. s__d__

6. b__k__

School Home

This unit targets the **long i** sound spelled **i-consonant-e**. Ask your child to read the spelling words aloud.

TEKS 1.22C Spell high-frequency words from a commonly used list.

A. Put the sounds together. Say the words and then write them.

1. l + ike = _____

2. h + ide = _____

3. r + ide = _____

bike

like

hike

hide

ride

side

B. Add **s** to a spelling word to tell about the pictures.

4.  +  _____

5.  + _____

6.  + _____

TEKS 1.22A Use phonological knowledge to match sounds to letters to construct known words. **1.22Bii** Use letter-sound patterns to spell: consonant-vowel-consonant-silent e (CVCe) words. **1.22C** Spell high-frequency words from a commonly used list. **1.22D** Spell base words with inflectional endings.

Write the missing spelling words.

In the City

I __1.__ living in the city.

I can __2.__ on a train.

I can __3.__ in the park.

I can __4.__ on the street.

I can lean on the __5.__ of the building and watch the people go by.

I can ride my __6.__ to the store.

bike
like
hike
hide
ride
side

1. _____

2. _____

3. _____

4. _____

5. _____

6. _____

TEKS 1.22C Spell high-frequency words from a commonly used list.

A. Underline the spelling words. Then write them on the lines below.

Me

I am six years old,
As happy as can be⊙
I can ride a bike,
And ̶Go on a hike.
I go round the side
In a game of hide.
My name is v̲ictor
And I like being me.

— Victor A. Wheeler

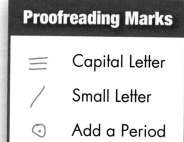

Proofreading Marks

☰	Capital Letter
/	Small Letter
⊙	Add a Period

bike

like

hike

hide

ride

side

1. _____

2. _____

3. _____

4. _____

5. _____

6. _____

B. Rewrite the poem. Make the changes shown by the proofreading marks.

C. Write a poem that tells about you. Try to use all the spelling words.

TEKS 1.22A Use phonological knowledge to match sounds to letters to construct known words. **1.22C** Spell high-frequency words from a commonly used list.

1. no

2. go

3. so

4. hope

5. rope

6. home

A. Write the spelling words that have **o** and **e**.

1. _____

2. _____

3. _____

B. Write the spelling words that end in **o**.

4. _____

5. _____

6. _____

School Home
This unit targets the **long o** sound spelled **o** and **o-consonant-e**. Ask your child to circle the **o-consonant-e** spelling pattern in the last three spelling words.

 TEKS 1.22C Spell high-frequency words from a commonly used list.

A. Use the clues to find spelling words. Write the words.

This word rhymes with **dome**.

1. _____

These words rhyme with each other, and they have a **silent e**.

2. _____   3. _____

B. Write the spelling words that end in **o** in a-b-c order.

4. _____

5. _____

6. _____

no

go

so

hope

rope

home

TEKS 1.22A Use phonological knowledge to match sounds to letters to construct known words. **1.22Bii** Use letter-sound patterns to spell: consonant-vowel-consonant-silent e (CVCe) words. **1.22C** Spell high-frequency words from a commonly used list.

A. Write the spelling words to finish the letter.

Dear Tim,

My __1.__ is in the desert. I __2.__ to a little school. Sometimes there is __3.__ rain for a long tim. It is __4.__ hot and dry. There are noot many plants. I wove this __5.__ for you. I __6.__ you like it.

Love,
Maria

no	
go	
so	
hope	
rope	
home	

1. _____   2. _____

3. _____   4. _____

5. _____   6. _____

B. Underline two words that are misspelled in the sentences above. Find the words in your dictionary. Write the correct words.

7. _____   8. _____

TEKS 1.22C Spell high-frequency words from a commonly used list. **1.22E** Use resources to find correct spellings.

153

Connections to WRITING

A. Underline the spelling words. Then write them on the lines below.

Long ago winters were bad for people on the plains. the wind blew the snow so hard no one could see. A farmer would tie a rope from his home to the barn He could get lost in the Snow if he let go. The farmer had hope that the snow would stop soon.

Proofreading Marks

☰	Capital Letter
/	Small Letter
⊙	Add a Period

no

go

so

hope

rope

home

1. _____

2. _____

3. _____

4. _____

5. _____

6. _____

B. Rewrite the sentences. Make the changes shown by the proofreading marks.

C. Write a story about winter. Try to use all the spelling words.

TEK 1.22C Spell high-frequency words from a commonly used list.

1. nose	Write the letters to finish each spelling word and name the picture.
2. rose	1. o e
3. bone	2. o e
4. note	3. o e
5. pole	4. o e
6. rode	5. o e
	6. o e

This unit targets the **long o** sound spelled **o-consonant-e**. Ask your child to circle the spelling words that rhyme.

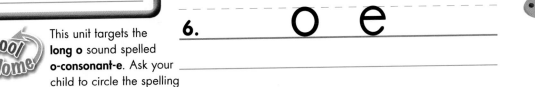

 TEKS 1.22A Use phonological knowledge to match sounds to letters to construct known words. **1.22Bii** Use letter-sound patterns to spell: consonant-vowel-consonant-silent e (CVCe) words. **1.22C** Spell high-frequency words from a commonly used list.

A. Change the **a** or the **i** to **o** and write the spelling word.

1. pale

_____

2. ride

_____

3. rise

_____

4. bane

_____

| nose |
| rose |
| bone |
| note |
| pole |
| rode |

B. Write the words that begin with the same sound as  .

5. _____

6. _____

 **TEKS 1.22A** Use phonological knowledge to match sounds to letters to construct known words. **1.22C** Spell high-frequency words from a commonly used list.

Write the silly sentences.

1. A bee __?__ on her __?__ .

2. A __?__ is on the __?__ .

3. A __?__ is on the __?__ .

nose
rose
bone
note
pole
rode

_____

1. _____.

_____

2. _____.

_____

3. _____.

TEKS 1.22C Spell high-frequency words from a commonly used list.

A. Underline the spelling words. Then write them on the lines below.

Gifts can be very special. A rose or other flower is nice. It's like a note that says "I love you." It's a treat for you and your nose⊙Some people would like to get a fishing pole. <u>if</u> you were a dog, a bone would be great. Once I got a /Bike as a gift. I rode it every day.

Proofreading Marks

≡	Capital Letter
/	Small Letter
⊙	Add a Period

nose
rose
bone
note
pole
rode

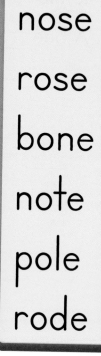

1. _____

2. _____

3. _____

4. _____

5. _____

6. _____

B. Rewrite the sentences. Make the changes shown by the proofreading marks.

C. Write about a gift you would like to give or get.
Use as many spelling words as you can.

TEK 1.22C Spell high-frequency words from a commonly used list.

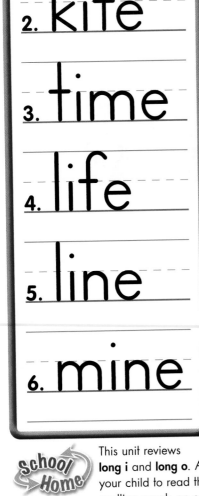

1. bite
2. kite
3. time
4. life
5. line
6. mine

Unit 26: **Long i: CVCe**

Fill in the blanks to write spelling words.

1. _ _ f _

2. m _ n _

3. b _ _ _ _

4. t _ _ e

5. k _ _ _

6. l _ n _

School Home — This unit reviews **long i** and **long o**. Ask your child to read the spelling words on each page aloud.

Review

1. bike
2. like
3. hike
4. hide
5. ride
6. side

Unit 27: **Long i: CVCe**

A. Write the words that end with **ide**.

1. _____   2. _____

3. _____

B. Write the words that end with **ike**.

4. _____   5. _____

6. _____

Review

1. no
2. go
3. so
4. hope
5. rope
6. home

Unit 28: Long o: o, CVCe

Circle the **long o** words. Write them.

1. hop

   hope _____

2. house

   home _____

3. rope

   romp _____

4. go

   got _____

5. so

   sock _____

6. not

   no _____

Review

1. nose
2. rose
3. bone
4. note
5. pole
6. rode

Unit 29: Long o: CVCe

A. Write the spelling words that end with **ose**.

1. _____

2. _____

B. Use the letter clue to write a spelling word.

3. p_____

4. _____d

5. _____t

6. b_____

1. do
2. you
3. zoo
4. use
5. room
6. soon

A. Write the spelling words with **oo**.

1. _____ 2. _____

3. _____

B. Write the spelling word with the $\overline{oo}$ sound spelled **o**.

4. _____

C. Write the spelling word with the y$\overline{oo}$ sound spelled **ou**.

5. _____

D. Write the spelling word with the y$\overline{oo}$ sound spelled **u_e**.

6. _____

School Home

This unit targets the $\overline{oo}$ and y$\overline{oo}$ sounds. Ask your child to use each spelling word in a sentence.

TEKS 1.22A Use phonological knowledge to match sounds to letters to construct known words. **1.22C** Spell high-frequency words from a commonly used list.

163

A. Write the spelling word that sounds like **u**
and the word that begins with **u**.

1. _____   2. _____

B. Write the spelling word that rhymes with **to** and has two letters.
Write the word that rhymes with **moon**.

3. _____   4. _____

C. Write **room** and **zoo** to show more than one.

5. _____   6. _____

do

you

zoo

use

room

soon

164

TEKS **1.22A** Use phonological knowledge to match sounds to letters to construct known words. **1.22C** Spell high-frequency words from a commonly used list. **1.22D** Spell base words with inflectional endings.

Write a spelling word to complete each sentence.

1. What can we __?__ ?

2. We will make a __?__ .

3. We can __?__ this box for a pool.

4. It has __?__ for seals.

5. Can __?__ help me find the tape?

6. Our zoo will __?__ be finished.

do

you

zoo

use

room

soon

1. _____

2. _____

3. _____

4. _____

5. _____

6. _____

TEKS 1.22C Spell high-frequency words from a commonly used list.

Connections to WRITING

Use proofreading marks to fix what you read. Add a letter or a word with ∧. Take away a letter or a word with ℯ. Start a paragraph with ⁋.

Proofreading Marks

≡	Capital Letter
/	Small Letter
∧	Add
ℯ	Delete
⊙	Add a Period
⁋	Indent

do
you
zoo
use
room
soon

A. Underline the spelling words. Then write them on the lines below.

Dear Aunt Lil,

⁋I do like the zoo. We went today. We always use a map map to find new animals. We will ∧see you soon. I want to show you my new room⊙

Love,
Jen

1. _____   2. _____

3. _____   4. _____

5. _____   6. _____

B. Rewrite the letter. Make the changes shown by the proofreading marks.

TEKS 1.22C Spell high-frequency words from a commonly used list.

1. back	
2. pack	
3. neck	
4. pick	
5. sock	
6. duck	

Finish the spelling word that names the picture.

1. _____ ck

2. _____ ck

3. _____ ck

4. _____ ck

5. _____ ck

6. _____ ck

School Home This unit targets final **ck**. Ask your child to read each word and circle **ck**.

TEKS 1.22A Use phonological knowledge to match sounds to letters to construct known words. **1.22C** Spell high-frequency words from a commonly used list.

A. Write letters in the blanks to complete each spelling word.

back
pack
neck
pick
sock
duck

1. ne__ __

_____

- - - - - - - - - - - - - - - -

_____

_____

2. b__ __k

_____

- - - - - - - - - - - - - - - -

_____

_____

3. p__c__

_____

- - - - - - - - - - - - - - - -

_____

_____

4. pa__ __

_____

- - - - - - - - - - - - - - - -

_____

_____

B. Add and write.

5. 1  + 1  = 2 _____

6. 1  + 1  = 2 _____

TEKS 1.22C Spell high-frequency words from a commonly used list. **1.22D** Spell base words with inflectional endings.

Write the missing spelling words.

Meg's Duck

Meg has a pet __1.__ . Its  __2.__

is brown and its  __3.__ is black. Meg let me

 __4.__ it up. I fed it a __5.__ of crackers.

When I put it down, it pecked at my __6.__ .

I guess it thought I was a bug!

back	
pack	
neck	
pick	
sock	
duck	

1. _____ 2. _____

3. _____ 4. _____

5. _____ 6. _____

TEKS 1.22C Spell high-frequency words from a commonly used list.

Connections to WRITING

A. Underline the spelling words. Then write them on the lines below.

¶A duck is a bird. Ducks spend a lot of time in water⊙They swim and dive to pick up their fo°d. Male mallards have a gray back with brown in the middle. the head is green. A white ring around the neck makes it look as if he hass̸ a sock on his head. The female is brown. She can pack about 12 eggs in her nest.

Proofreading Marks

≡	Capital Letter
/	Small Letter
∧	Add
ℓ	Delete
⊙	Add a Period
¶	Indent

back

pack

neck

pick

sock

duck

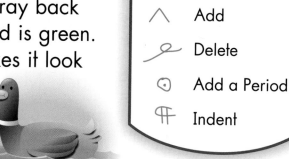

1. _____

2. _____

3. _____

4. _____

5. _____

6. _____

B. Rewrite the sentences. Make the changes shown by the proofreading marks.

C. Write more about mallard ducks. Use as many spelling words as you can. Check your spelling in a dictionary.

TEK 1.22C Spell high-frequency words from a commonly used list.
1.22E Use resources to find correct spellings.

1. ship	
2. shop	
3. show	
4. dish	
5. wish	
6. push	

A. Write the word that goes with the meanings. Circle **sh** in each word.

1.

or "to look for things to buy"

_____

2.

or "to send"

_____

3.

or "to let someone see something"

_____

4.

or "to put food out"

_____

B. Circle the spelling words. Then write them.

5. "I wish I had help!"

_____

6. "I will help you push."

_____

School Home

This unit targets the **sh** sound. Ask your child to write each spelling word and circle **sh**.

TEKS 1.22A Use phonological knowledge to match sounds to letters to construct known words. **1.22C** Spell high-frequency words from a commonly used list.

1–2. Write the spelling words that rhyme with  .

_____

_____

_____

_____

3. Write the spelling word that rhymes with .

_____

_____

4. Write the spelling word that rhymes with .

_____

_____

5. Write the spelling word that means the opposite of **pull**.

_____

_____

6. Write the spelling word with the **long o** sound.

_____

_____

ship
shop
show
dish
wish
push

TEKS 1.22A Use phonological knowledge to match sounds to letters to construct known words.
1.22C Spell high-frequency words from a commonly used list.

Connections to READING

A. Write the missing spelling words.

ship
shop
show
dish
wish
push

1. We are going on a _____.

2. Mom will _____ mee our room.

3. I kan _____ the buttons.

4. I _____ I could steer.

5–6. We can get a _____ in the _____.

B. Find two words above that are misspelled. Draw a line under each word.
Check your dictionary. Fix and write the words.

7. _____

8. _____

TEKS 1.22C Spell high-frequency words from a commonly used list. **1.22E** Use resources to find correct spellings.

Connections to WRITING

A. Underline the spelling words. Then write them on the lines below.

My Dream

I dream I am on a trip.
I am on a great big ship.
I have ^to^ wash every dish,
And shop to fill every wish.
i push a cart from place to place.
And always show a ̶S̶miling face.
When I wake up I find it's true.
I am a member of the crew⊙

Proofreading Marks

≡	Capital Letter
/	Small Letter
∧	Add
ℯ	Delete
⊙	Add a Period
⁋	Indent

ship
shop
show
dish
wish
push

1. _____

2. _____

3. _____

4. _____

5. _____

6. _____

B. Rewrite the poem. Make the changes shown by the proofreading marks.

C. Write a poem about a dream or a wish. Use as many spelling words as you can.

TEKS 1.22C Spell high-frequency words from a commonly used list.

1. that
2. then
3. this
4. bath
5. path
6. with

A. Use each clue to write a spelling word that begins with **th**.

1. rhymes with **hat**

2. a time word

3. ends with **s**

B. Write a spelling word that ends with **th** and names the picture.

4.

5.

6.

This unit targets the **th** sound. Ask your child to write each spelling word and circle **th**.

TEKS 1.22A Use phonological knowledge to match sounds to letters to construct known words. **1.22C** Spell high-frequency words from a commonly used list.

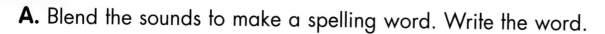
A. Blend the sounds to make a spelling word. Write the word.

1. th + is = _____

2. th + at = _____

3. th + en = _____

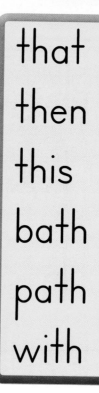

that

then

this

bath

path

with

B. Use the clues to find the spelling word. Write the word.

4. ● four letters ■ three sounds
   ▲ starts with **b**

5. ● three sounds ■ **short i**
   ▲ starts like **win**

6. ● four letters ■ three sounds
   ▲ **short a**

TEKS 1.22A Use phonological knowledge to match sounds to letters to construct known words. **1.22C** Spell high-frequency words from a commonly used list.

Write spelling words to finish the story.

1. Jimmy will play ___?___ me.

2. Will you hand me ___?___ pot?

3. Oh, ___?___ it will be your turn to cook.

4. We will take ___?___ cake to Mom.

5. "Did you make that ___?___?"

6. "It is time for your ___?___!"

that
then
this
bath
path
with

1. _____

2. _____

3. _____

4. _____

5. _____

6. _____

TEKS 1.22C Spell high-frequency words from a commonly used list.

177

A. Underline the spelling words. Then write them on the lines below.

¶In this forest there is a path⊙See that bird. It takes a bath in the puddle. Look at the deer. She is with her baby. See this turtle. It is going to its home in ~~in~~ the pond. Then it will be ~~T~~ime for us to go home.

Proofreading Marks

≡	Capital Letter
/	Small Letter
∧	Add
ℯ	Delete
⊙	Add a Period
¶	Indent

that

then

this

bath

path

with

1. _____

2. _____

3. _____

4. _____

5. _____

6. _____

B. Rewrite the sentences. Make the changes shown by the proofreading marks.

C. Write about a path you have walked or would like to walk. Use as many spelling words as you can. Check your spelling in a dictionary.

🟥 **TEKS 1.22C** Spell high-frequency words from a commonly used list. **1.22E** Use resources to find correct spellings.

Review

1. do
2. you
3. zoo
4. use
5. room
6. soon

Unit 31: Long u: o͞o, yo͞o

Fill in the blanks to write each spelling word.

1. z__ __

2. s__ __n

3. d__

4. r__ __m

5. __ s __

6. y __ __

 School Home

This unit reviews the o͞o and yo͞o sounds, **ck**, **sh**, and **th**. Ask your child to read the spelling words on each page aloud.

Review

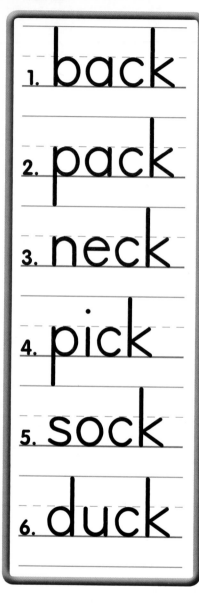

1. back
2. pack
3. neck
4. pick
5. sock
6. duck

Unit 32: **Final ck**

Change the last letter in each word to **ck**. Write the spelling word. Then draw a line to match the word with a picture.

_____

1. son _____

2. pat _____

3. dug _____

4. pin _____

5. bad _____

6. net _____

Review

1. ship
2. shop
3. show
4. dish
5. wish
6. push

Unit 33: Digraph: sh

A. Write the words that end with **sh** like .

1. _____

2. _____

3. _____

B. Write the words that start with **sh** like  .

4. _____

5. _____

6. _____

Review

1. that
2. then
3. this
4. bath
5. path
6. with

Unit 34: Digraph: th

A. Write the spelling words that end with **th**.

1. _____

2. _____

3. _____

B. Complete each spelling word.

4. __ __ is

5. __ __ en

6. __ __ at

Challenge Words

ant	lap	tag	pants

A. Write the word from the box that rhymes with the picture name.

1.  _____ The ants have on

_ _ _ _ _ _ _ _ _ _ _

_____ .

2. _____ The cap is on her

_ _ _ _ _ _ _ _ _ _ _

_____ .

3. _____ Grant sat on an

_ _ _ _ _ _ _ _ _ _ _

_____ .

4. _____ This bag has a

_ _ _ _ _ _ _ _ _ _ _

_____ .

B. Complete the sentence.

 _____

_ _ _ _ _ _ _ _ _ _ _

5–6. The _____ is on my _____ .

_____

TEKS 1.22A Use phonological knowledge to match sounds to letters to construct known words. **1.22C** Spell high-frequency words from a commonly used list.

Challenge Words

| bag | pan | mat | lamp |

A. Write the word that goes with the others.

1. pot  skillet

_____

2. pail box

_____

3. candle flashlight

_____

4. rug tiles

_____

B. Complete the sentence.

5–6. The _____ is in the _____.

 TEKS 1.22C Spell high-frequency words from a commonly used list.

Challenge Words

hen	den	wet	fed

A. Complete each word.

Jan _____f_____ the _____w_____ _____h_____ in the _____d_____.

B. Write a sentence using **hen** and **wet**.
Write a sentence using **den** and **fed**.

_____

_____

_____

_____

TEKS 1.22C Spell high-frequency words from a commonly used list.

Challenge Words

| led | vest | mend | mess |

Write the words to tell about each picture.

1–2. Did the robin _____ her old _____?

3–4. Jan _____ Tim out of the _____.

TEKS 1.22C Spell high-frequency words from a commonly used list.

Challenge Words

sip	lid	tip	wig

Write a word from the box to complete each sentence.

1. I can ___?___ from the glass.

2. The ___?___ fits the pan.

3. Nan has a ___?___ .

4.  The ___?___ of the pen is bad.

TEKS 1.22C Spell high-frequency words from a commonly used list.

187

Challenge Words

| bib | rip | pin | zip |

Write a word from the box to finish each rhyme.

1. For first place you will win a shiny, purple

_____

_____ .

_____

2. My old jacket has a rip and now it will no longer

_____

_____ .

_____

3. The little baby in her crib wears a new, lacy

_____

_____ .

_____

4. With your scissors you can snip. With your fingers you can

_____

_____ .

_____

TEKS 1.22A Use phonological knowledge to match sounds to letters to construct known words. **1.22C** Spell high-frequency words from a commonly used list.

Challenge Words

| ox | cod | jog | trot |

Write a word from the box to complete each sentence.
Then circle the word in the same sentence that rhymes with it.

1. An _____ has horns, but a fox does not.

2. A _____ has fins, and I can catch one with a rod.

3. Horses _____ but fish do not.

4. People _____ through sun, rain, or fog.

TEKS 1.22C Spell high-frequency words from a commonly used list.

Challenge Words

hog	rod	jot	body

Write a word from the box to solve each riddle.

1. I am a pole used for fishing. My name rhymes with **cod**.

_____

- - - - - - - - - - - - - - - - - - -

_____

2. I am another name for a pig. My name rhymes with a pet you might have.

_____

- - - - - - - - - - - - - - - - - - -

_____

3. I go with **any** and **every**.

_____

- - - - - - - - - - - - - - - - - - -

_____

4. I start like **jog** and rhyme with **dot**.

_____

- - - - - - - - - - - - - - - - - - -

_____

TEKS 1.22A Use phonological knowledge to match sounds to letters to construct known words. **1.22C** Spell high-frequency words from a commonly used list.

dug	hum	snug	bump

Write a word to complete each sentence.

1. Pip __?__ in the sand.

2. Dad hit a big __?__

3. Cal can __?__ in the tub.

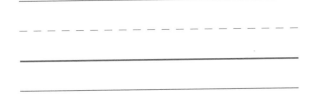

4. I was __?__ in the bag.

TEKS 1.22C Spell high-frequency words from a commonly used list.

191

Challenge Words

cub	bud	pup	hut

Write a word to finish each sentence.

1. A small _____ house is a

_____ .

2. A small _____ dog is a

_____ .

3. A small closed _____ flower is a

_____ .

4. A small _____ bear is a

_____ .

TEKS 1.22C Spell high-frequency words from a commonly used list.

Challenge Words

mix	wag	pop	bend

Write the word that fits each clue.

1. to move from side to side

_____

- - - - - - - - - - - - - - -

_____

2. to make a loud, bursting sound

_____

- - - - - - - - - - - - - - -

_____

3. to blend together

_____

- - - - - - - - - - - - - - -

_____

4. to make something curved

_____

- - - - - - - - - - - - - - -

_____

TEKS 1.22C Spell high-frequency words from a commonly used list.

Challenge Words

ago	easy	goes	only

Complete the missing words.

A long time __1.__ there were no phones. It was not __2.__ to get a message to someone. Now you __3.__ have to push a few buttons. Your voice __4.__ where you want it to!

1. a _____

2. e _____

3. o _____

4. g _____

TEKS 1.22C Spell high-frequency words from a commonly used list.

Challenge Words

Initial Consonant Blends

| grab | slip | snap | plug |

Complete each word to finish each sentence.

1. The dog will __?__ at the bug.

s _____

2. I can __?__ your hand.

g _____

3. Will the pig __?__ in the mud.

s _____

4. Let Mom __?__ in the lamp.

p _____

TEKS 1.22C Spell high-frequency words from a commonly used list.

| post | stir | rust | stiff |

Write the missing words.

1–2. He will _____ the paint with a _____ paddle.

3–4. Ned will paint the _____. It has _____ on it.

TEKS 1.22C Spell high-frequency words from a commonly used list.

Challenge Words

| cards | chips | pumps | twins |

Write the missing words.

1. The two boys are __?__.

2. I got lots of __?__ on my birthday.

3. The cup has two __?__ in it.

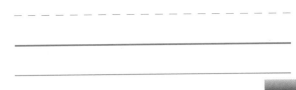

4. Dad __?__ gas into the car.

TEKS 1.22C Spell high-frequency words from a commonly used list.

Challenge Words

| mowing | packing | bending | picking |

Look at each picture. Write the best word.

1. ___?___ down

2. ___?___ plums

3. ___?___ a bag

4. ___?___ grass

TEKS 1.22C Spell high-frequency words from a commonly used list.

| ape | wake | mane | tame |

Write words to complete the sentences.

I had a  dream about a

 lion and an __1.__ .

The lion was __2.__ . The ape

was not. The ape pulled on the lion's

 __3.__ . The lion

made a loud noise. The noise made me

__4.__ up.

1. _____

2. _____

3. _____

4. _____

TEKS 1.22C Spell high-frequency words from a commonly used list.

Challenge Words

| lace | lane | date | vase |

Write a word to name each picture.

1. _____

2. _____

3. _____

4. _____

TEKS 1.22C Spell high-frequency words from a commonly used list.

| beet | peel | peek | deed |

Write a word to finish each sentence.

1. Let me __?__ into the box.

_____

_____

2. Will you __?__ his orange?

_____

_____

3. I ate the big __?__ .

_____

_____

4. When you do something kind for someone, you do a good __?__ .

_____

_____

TEKS 1.22C Spell high-frequency words from a commonly used list.

201

Challenge Words

Long e: ee

| weed | creek | sweep | cheek |

Write the word that fits each group.

1. dust, , mop, , ___?___

2. nose, 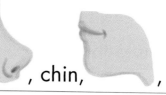, chin, , ___?___

3. river, stream, ___?___

4. grass, , flower, , ___?___

TEKS 1.22C Spell high-frequency words from a commonly used list.

Challenge Words

tide	vine	pine	hive

Write a word that rhymes with the word in ( ) to complete the sentences.

1. Did you sit under the __?__ tree? **(fine)**

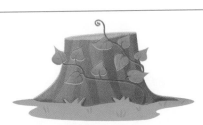

2. The jellyfish came in with the __?__ . **(ride)**

3. The busy bees are in the __?__ . **(five)**

4. The deer like to eat this __?__ . **(line)**

TEKS 1.22A Use phonological knowledge to match sounds to letters to construct known words. **1.22C** Spell high-frequency words from a commonly used list.

203

| wide | rice | dive | wipe |

Write a word to complete each sentence.

1. **W**ise **W**illy opened the **w**indow ___?___ .

2. **R**ick's pet **r**at ate the ___?___ !

3. **D**o **d**ucks ___?___ for their **d**inner?

4. **W**e will ___?___ the **w**agon **w**ith **w**ax.

TEKS 1.22A Use phonological knowledge to match sounds to letters to construct known words. **1.22C** Spell high-frequency words from a commonly used list.

Challenge Words

| cone | dome | hole | hose |

Write the missing words.

1. It lives in a __?__ in the ground.

2. Did you get wet from the __?__?

3. Look at the big __?__ on that building!

4. I found this pine __?__ under the tree.

TEKS 1.22C Spell high-frequency words from a commonly used list.

205

Challenge Words

| code | woke | mole | stove |

Write a word to finish the sentence and tell about the picture.

1. My cat __?__ me up.

2. The __?__ dug a hole.

3. We will make up a secret __?__ .

4. The pot is on the __?__ .

TEKS 1.22C Spell high-frequency words from a commonly used list.

Challenge Words

moon	broom	spoon	stool

Write the word that names each picture.

1.

_____

- - - - - - - - - - - - - - -

_____

2.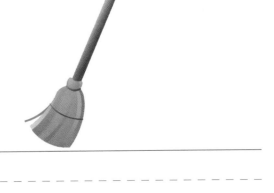

_____

- - - - - - - - - - - - - - -

_____

3.

_____

- - - - - - - - - - - - - - -

_____

4.

_____

- - - - - - - - - - - - - - -

_____

TEKS 1.22A Use phonological knowledge to match sounds to letters to construct known words. **1.22C** Spell high-frequency words from a commonly used list.

Challenge Words

| tuck | quack | crack | cluck |

Write the words to finish the sentences.

Mother Hen and Mother Duck carefully __1.__ their eggs under them. They hear a loud __2.__ ! Mother Hen says, " __3.__ !" Mother Duck says, " __4.__ !" See what has happened!

1. _____

2. _____

3. _____

4. _____

TEKS 1.22C Spell high-frequency words from a commonly used list.

| shut | crash | hush | shake |

Write a word that goes with the action in the picture.

1. _____

2. _____

3. _____

4. _____

TEKS 1.22A Use phonological knowledge to match sounds to letters to construct known words. **1.22C** Spell high-frequency words from a commonly used list.

209

Challenge Words

| thin | thump | thud | booth |

Cross out the wrong word. Write the word that rhymes.

1. First we heard a lump!

_____

- - - - - - - - - - - - - - -

_____

2. Then there was a loud mud!

_____

- - - - - - - - - - - - - - -

_____

3. I saw a tin shadow on the wall!

_____

- - - - - - - - - - - - - - -

_____

4. This is a scary tooth!

_____

- - - - - - - - - - - - - - -

_____

TEKS 1.22C Spell high-frequency words from a commonly used list.

Spelling Study Strategy

Look, Say

Look at the word.

Say the letters. Think about how each sound is spelled.

Cover, See

Cover the word with your hand or close your eyes.

See the word in your mind. Spell the word to yourself.

Write, Check

Write the word.

Check your spelling.

Using the Dictionary — A-B-C Order

Words in a dictionary are in a-b-c order. Words that start with **a** are first. Words that start with **b** are next. Words that start with **z** are last.

Fill in the blanks to write the **abc**'s in order.

a   b   _____   d   e   _____   g   _____   i   j

_____   _____   m   n   _____   p   q   r   s

_____   u   _____   w   _____   y   _____

Read the words below. Then copy them to show the order you would find them in a dictionary.

zoo   ant   duck

1. _____

2. _____

3. _____

Using the Dictionary

Guide Words

There are two words at the top of each dictionary page. These words are called **guide words**.

The first guide word is the first word on that page. ↓

The other guide word is the last word on that page. ↘

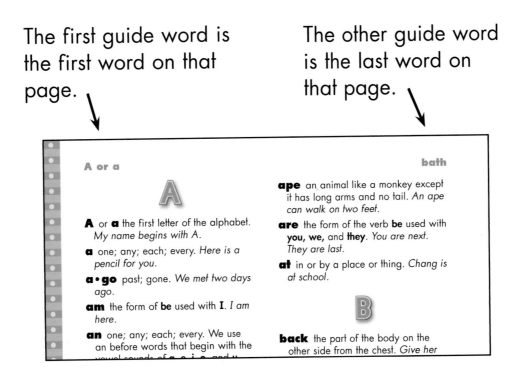

A or a

A

A or **a** the first letter of the alphabet. *My name begins with A.*

a one; any; each; every. *Here is a pencil for you.*

a•go past; gone. *We met two days ago.*

am the form of **be** used with **I**. *I am here.*

an one; any; each; every. We use an before words that begin with the vowel sounds of

bath

ape an animal like a monkey except it has long arms and no tail. *An ape can walk on two feet.*

are the form of the verb **be** used with **you, we,** and **they.** *You are next. They are last.*

at in or by a place or thing. *Chang is at school.*

B

back the part of the body on the other side from the chest. *Give her*

All the words on this page fall between the guide words in a-b-c order.

Circle the words that you would find on the dictionary page above.

| ant | dog | milk | fall | are | back |

Using the Dictionary Entries

Here is an entry from your **Spelling Dictionary**.

pet an animal kept with people.
A cat may make a good pet.

A dictionary **entry** is all the information about one word. An entry is the **entry word,** the **definition,** and the **sample sentence**.

1. The entry word is the word you are looking up.

_____

- - - - - - - - - - - - - -

Write the entry word here. _____

_____

2. The definition tells what the entry word means.

Circle the definition in the entry above.

3. The sample sentence uses the entry word. It helps you understand the word.

Underline the sample sentence in the entry above.

4. Circle the pair of guide words that could be on the page with **pet**.

a • back   **soon • sweep**   **path • pop**

 Entries

Here is an entry from your **Spelling Dictionary**.

> **frog** a small animal with webbed feet that lives near water. *A frog can jump far.*

An **entry word** is the word you are looking up. It is the first word in the entry. The entry word shows you how to spell the word. Entry words are in **bold type**.

1. Circle the entry word in the entry above.

The **definition** is the next part of an entry. The definition tells you what the entry word means.

2. Underline the definition in the entry above.

Here is another entry from your **Spelling Dictionary**.

> **note a.** a very short message or letter. *Let's write Mom a note.* **b.** a sign in music. *This is a quarter note.*

Sometimes an entry word can have more than one meaning. It will have more than one definition in the entry. Find two definitions for the word **note**.

3. Draw one line under the first definition.

4. Draw two lines under the second definition.

Using the Dictionary
Sample Sentences

The **sample sentence** in a dictionary entry can be very helpful. The sample sentence uses the entry word in a sentence. The sentence can help you understand the entry word. It can help you know how to use the word. Sample sentences are in *italic type*.

1. Underline the sample sentence in this entry from your **Spelling Dictionary**.

> **moon** the body that shines in the night sky.
> *A full moon looks like a big circle.*

An entry also shows different **forms** of words. An entry will show the forms of action words. Forms are in **dark type**.

2. Underline the forms in the entry below.

> **hope** (**hopes, hoped, hop•ing**) to wish or expect.
> *I hope you will visit us soon.*

An entry will show the plurals of naming words. **Plural** means "more than one." Plurals are in **dark type**.

3. Underline the plural form in the entry below.

> **bus** (**bus•es** *pl.*) a long car or van that can carry many people.
> *We ride a bus to school.*

Using the Dictionary

The **Spelling Dictionary** is the place to learn many helpful things about the spelling words.

The **entry** is the entry word, the definition, and the sample sentence.

The **entry word** is the spelling word you look up. Entry words are listed in a-b-c order.

The **definition** tells you what the word means.

ant

ant a small insect that lives in the ground or in wood. *An ant lives and works in a group.*

The **sample sentence** shows how the word is used in a sentence.

A or **a** the first letter of the alphabet. *My name begins with A.*

a one; any; each; every. *Here is a pencil for you.*

a•go past; gone. *We met two days ago.*

am the form of **be** used with **I**. *I am here.*

an one; any; each; every. We use an before words that begin with the vowel sounds of **a, e, i, o,** and **u**. *I ate an apple an hour ago.*

and a. with; together with; besides. *She likes to sing and dance.* b. added to. *In math, 4 and 5 are 9.*

ant a small insect that lives in the ground or in wood. *An ant lives and works in a group.*

ant

ape an animal like a monkey except it has long arms and no tail. *An ape can walk on two feet.*

are the form of the verb **be** used with **you, we,** and **they**. *You are next. They are last.*

at in or by a place or thing. *Chang is at school.*

back the part of the body on the other side from the chest. *Give her a pat on the back.*

bad (**worse, worst; bad•ly**) not good, right, or healthy. *Eating too much is bad for you.*

bag a sack; a container made of soft material. *Scott will take the bag with food in it.*

bake (**bakes, baked, bak•ing**) to cook in an oven. *We bake bread.*

bath a washing of the whole body. *We gave our dog a bath.*

be (am, are, is, was, were, been, be•ing) **a.** to equal. *Anna answered, "2 and 3 are 5."* **b.** to happen. *What time will the game be?*

bed a thing to sleep or rest on. *Meg can make her bed.*

bed

beet a plant grown for its juicy root. *He ate the red beet.*

bend (bends, bent, bend•ing) **a.** to make something curve. *Help me bend this wire.* **b.** to stoop or lean over. *Can you bend and touch your toes?*

best better than all others. *That was the best lunch I ever had.*

bib a cloth tied under a baby's chin to keep his or her clothing clean. *The baby's bib was full of food.*

big large. *Our school is big.*

bike a bicycle. *Juan rides his bike.*

bit past tense of **bite**. *He bit into the apple.*

bite (bites, bit, bit•ten or bit, bit•ing) to grab, hold, or cut with the teeth. *When I lost my front teeth, it was hard to bite.*

bod•y (bod•ies *pl.*) all the parts that make up a person or an animal. *Take good care of your body.*

bone a hard part inside the body; a part of the skeleton. *Your longest bone is in your leg.*

booth **a.** a stand where something is sold. *Our class ran an art booth at the school fair.* **b.** a closed place. *Use the phone in that booth.*

box (box•es *pl.*) a case to hold things. *I have a toy box.*

box

broom a brush with a long handle, used for sweeping. *You can use the broom to sweep the walk.*

bud the small beginning of a flower or leaf. *That bud will be a rose.*

bug (bugs *pl.*) an insect, usually one that crawls. *Even a small bug can crawl fast.*

bump **a.** to knock or hit against something. *Try not to bump into the wall.* **b.** a raised place. *The bump in the road makes the car bounce.*

bus (bus•es *pl.*) a long car or van that can carry many people. *We ride a bus to school.*

but **a.** yet; however. *I will come, but I want to eat lunch first.* **b.** except. *We can go any day but Monday.*

came past tense of **come**. *They came to see us last week.*

can (could) **a.** to know how or to be able to. *He can play the piano.* **b.** a metal container. *Here is a can of peas.*

cards small pieces of stiff paper. *We wrote the letters on separate cards.*

cat (cats *pl.*) **a.** a small furry animal that can purr. *Our cat loves to sit on my lap.* **b.** any larger animal that is also a part of the cat family. *A lion is a cat.*

cat

cheek the side of the face below the eye. *She had a little smudge on her cheek.*

chips small pieces broken or cut off something. *Glue these chips back onto the cup.*

cluck a sound made by a chicken. *When a hen calls her chicks, it sounds like "cluck, cluck."*

cod a big fish often used for food. *Cod live in cold water.*

code a set of signals for sending messages. *Our club made up a secret code.*

come (comes, came, come, com•ing) **a.** to move closer; arrive. *Come over to my house.* **b.** to happen. *Our birthdays come once a year.*

cone **a.** an object that is round at one end and pointed at the other. *She made a cone of paper.* **b.** the seed pod of an evergreen tree. *That pine cone grew on a white pine tree.*

crack (cracks, cracked, crack•ing) **a.** to break or split without snapping apart. *The glass may crack when I wash it.* **b.** to make a sudden snapping noise. *Did you hear the thunder crack?*

crash the very loud noise of something falling, breaking, or hitting. *The tree fell with a loud crash.*

creek a small stream. *The ducks swim in the creek.*

cub a young bear, lion, or wolf. *We saw a bear cub at the zoo.*

cub

cut (cuts, cut, cut•ting) to split with something sharp. *Let's cut this apple in half.*

dad a short word for **father**. *My dad took us for a walk.*

date the time when something happens. *July 4 is an important date.*

deed an act; a thing done. *Helping Jill clean her room was a good deed.*

deep far down or back. *Big fish swim in deep water.*

den **a.** the home of a wild animal. *The lion cubs stay near their den.* **b.** a small room where one can read, relax, or work. *Mother is watching TV in the den.*

did past tense of **do**. *I did my homework last night.*

dig (digs, dug, dig•ging) to make a hole in the ground. *Dogs dig holes with their front paws.*

dish (dish•es *pl.*) **a.** something that holds food. *Put the dish on the table.* **b.** to serve food. *Mom will dish out the green beans.*

dive (dives, dived or dove, div•ing) to jump headfirst into water. *Seals dive to catch fish.*

do (does, did, done, do•ing) to act, make, perform, or carry out. *Everyone in the class will do something different.*

dome a round roof or cover. *Dad put the cheese under a glass dome.*

dot **a.** a small round spot. *There was a dot of ink on my new shirt.* **b.** to mark with a small round spot. *Be sure to dot that **i**.*

duck a swimming bird with webbed feet, a short neck, and a flat bill. *The duck swam in the pond.*

duck

dug past tense of **dig**. *Dan dug a deep hole.*

eas•y not hard to get or do. *A toy on wheels is easy to pull.*

fast able to act or move quickly. *We can run fast.*

fed past tense of **feed**. *I fed the dog.*

feed (feeds, fed, feed•ing) to give food to. *We must feed the horses.*

feel (feels, felt, feel•ing) **a.** to touch. *Feel the soft fur of the cat.* **b.** to have the feeling of being. *I feel cold.* **c.** to have an emotion. *I feel sad.*

feet the parts of the body at the end of the legs. *I can stand on two feet.*

fix (fix•es, fixed, fix•ing) to repair or mend. *Grandpa can fix that broken toy.*

fox (**fox•es** *pl.*) a wild animal like a dog but with a bushy tail. *The fox ran into the forest.*

fox

frog a small animal with webbed feet that lives near water. *A frog can jump far.*

fun a good time; happy play. *We had fun at the zoo.*

game **a.** a way to play that follows rules. *Let's have a game of tag.* **b.** the things needed to play a game. *Where is your game of checkers?*

gate an opening like a door in a fence or wall. *She closed the garden gate.*

gave past tense of **give**. *We gave Mr. Russo a flower.*

get (**gets, got, got** or **got•ten, get•ting**) **a.** to come to have; to receive. *Our class will get new desks.* **b.** to bring. *I will get you a glass of milk.*

give (**gives, gave, giv•en, giv•ing**) to hand over; to let have. *I will give you this ball.*

go (**goes, went, gone, go•ing**) to move. *Let's go to your house to play.*

goes past tense of **go**. *This car goes fast.*

got past tense of **get**. *She got some carrots for a snack.*

grab (grabs, grabbed, grab•bing) to take hold of suddenly. *The boys grab their coats and run for the bus.*

grin (grins, grinned, grin•ning) to smile broadly. *The teacher may grin at my joke.*

had past tense of **have**. *We had fun at the park.*

has a form of **have**. *She has a sunny smile.*

hat a covering for the head; a cap. *My hat keeps my ears warm.*

hat

have (has, had, hav•ing) to own; to possess. *I have a red cap.*

he that boy or man. *He is a good boy.*

hen a female chicken or other bird. *Your hen can lay eggs.*

hide (hides, hid, hid•den or **hid**, hid•ing) to put or keep out of sight. *Let's hide the gifts quickly.*

hike **a.** a long walk. *We took a hike in the woods.* **b.** (hikes, hiked, hik•ing) to take a long walk. *Let's hike up that hill.*

him that boy or man. *Mike looked hungry, so I gave him an apple.*

his belonging to a boy or a man. *Ted likes to play with his dog.*

hive a box or other place where bees live. *Can you see any honey in the hive?*

hog a full-grown pig. *The hog eats lots of corn.*

hog

hole an opening or empty space. *A nail makes a hole in the wall.*

home the place where a person lives. *My home is an apartment.*

hop (hops, hopped, hop•ping) to move by jumping lightly. *Rabbits hop quickly.*

hope (hopes, hoped, hop•ing) to wish or expect. *I hope you will visit us soon.*

hose a rubber or plastic tube that carries water. *Mom used the hose to water the garden.*

hot very warm; having a high temperature. *The stove is hot.*

hug (hugs, hugged, hug•ging) to put the arms around something. *I hug my brother.*

hum (hums, hummed, hum•ming) to sing with the lips closed. *All day she liked to hum the new song.*

hush (hush•es, hushed, hush•ing) to make still or quiet. *See if you can hush the baby.*

hut a little house or cabin that is plain and simple. *We camped in huts.*

I me; myself; the person talking. *I am learning to spell.*

if **a.** whether. *Do you know if Carmen is coming?* **b.** though. *Even if it rains, we'll still go.*

in **a.** inside. *We live in town.* **b.** during. *It rained in the morning.*

is a form of **be**. *Kevin is tall.*

it that thing. *It is my book.*

jet a kind of plane with a strong engine. *The big jet took off with a loud roar.*

job the work that one does. *Taking out the trash is my job.*

jog (jogs, jogged, jog•ging) to run at a slow, steady pace. *Mrs. Morgan likes to jog every day to keep fit.*

jot (jots, jot•ted, jot•ting) to write something quickly. *Jot down this name on your list.*

keep (keeps, kept, keep•ing) **a.** to hold on to; to save. *Kim wants to keep all her old schoolwork.* **b.** to let stay; to have. *Todd can keep his socks in the top drawer.*

kite a paper or cloth toy that can fly in the air on the end of a long string. *My kite is red.*

kite

lace fine threads woven together in an open pattern. *Her dress was trimmed with white lace.*

lake an inland body of water. *We saw a sailboat on the lake.*

lamp an object that gives light. *Turn on the lamp.*

lamp

lane a narrow path or road. *We walked down the lane.*

lap the top part of a person's legs when sitting down. *Dad held the baby on his lap.*

lead (leads, led, lead•ing) to show the way; to take. *Will you please lead the dog back home?*

led past tense of **lead**. *We led the horse to the barn.*

leg the part of the body used for standing and walking. *We put our pants on one leg at a time.*

let (lets, let, let•ting) to allow; to permit. *Please let me go to the park.*

lid a top or cover. *He put the lid back on the pan.*

life being alive. *We study the life of plants.*

like a. the same as; similar to. *Marie is like a sister to me.* b. (likes, liked, lik•ing) to enjoy. *I like the new family next door.*

line a. a long thin mark. *Draw a line on the paper.* b. a row of persons or things. *We stood in a line.*

made past tense of **make**. *We made lunch on Monday.*

make (makes, made, mak•ing)
a. to put together; to build, form, or shape. *Dad can make a great pie.*
b. to cause. *Singing can make me feel happy.*

man (men *pl.*) an adult male person. *Mr. Green is a nice man.*

mane the long hair that grows on the back of the neck of a lion or horse. *A lion's mane makes him look important.*

mat a piece of fabric or woven straw; a small rug. *Wipe your feet on the mat near the door.*

me I; myself; the person talking. *Eric will go with Ann and me.*

meet (meets, met, meet•ing) to come face to face with; to come together. *I'll meet you down at the corner.*

men more than one man. *We watched the men working.*

men

mend (mends, mend•ed, mend•ing) to repair; to fix. *Can you mend the hole in the roof?*

mess a dirty or sloppy state of things. *My room was a mess before I cleaned it.*

met past tense of meet. *We met the new girl.*

mine belonging to me. *This box is mine.*

mix (mix•es, mixed, mix•ing) to put different things together. *I will mix nuts and raisins to make a snack.*

mole a small animal with smooth fur and small eyes that lives underground. *A mole has long claws.*

mom a short word for **mother**. *My mom has a good job.*

moon the body that shines in the night sky. *A full moon looks like a big circle.*

mop a. a long-handled tool used to clean floors. *This mop has a sponge on one end.* b. (mops, mopped, mop•ping) to wipe with a mop or cloth. *Please mop up the water.*

mow•ing form of **mow**. cutting the grass. *She is mowing the lawn this morning.*

must to have to. *You must come home at six.*

name a. a word or words to call a person, place, or thing. *His name is Ryan.* b. (names, named, nam•ing) to give a name to; to call. *They will name the boy after his grandfather.*

neck the part of the body that joins the head to the shoulders. *A giraffe has a very long neck.*

net a fabric with small holes. *He can catch a fish in his net.*

net

no a. the opposite of **yes**. *I voted "no" in a loud voice.* b. not any. *The dog had no food until we got home.*

nose the part of the face just above the mouth. *You smell with your nose.*

not a word that says **no**. *It is not a sunny day.*

note **a.** a very short message or letter. *Let's write Mom a note.* **b.** a sign in music. *That is a quarter note.*

nut a dry fruit or seed with a hard shell. *I ate one nut.*

nut

of **a.** belonging to. *The roof of the house is brown.* **b.** made from. *The birds live in a nest of twigs.*

on **a.** above and held up by. *The lamp is on the table.* **b.** about. *I have a book on kites.* **c.** in use; not off. *She turned the radio on.*

on•ly **a.** single; by itself. *This is my only shirt with stripes.* **b.** no more than; just. *We have only one hour to get ready.*

ox (ox•en *pl.*) a heavy bull used as a work animal. *The ox can pull a cart.*

pack **a.** (packs, packed, pack•ing) to put carefully in a box or trunk. *Help me pack my suitcase.* **b.** a soft bag carried on the back. *My pack is heavy.*

pan a container used for cooking. *Use a small pan to heat the soup.*

pants a piece of clothing that covers each leg separately. *I wear pants.*

path a narrow trail or track. *The path leads up the hill.*

peek (peeks, peeked, peek•ing) to take a quick look. *Close your eyes and don't peek.*

peel (peels, peeled, peel•ing) to take off the skin or outer layer. *We will peel the orange.*

pen a. a tool used for writing in ink. *My pen has blue ink.* **b.** a closed place to keep animals. *That pig lives in a pen.*

pen

pet an animal kept with people. *A cat may make a good pet.*

pick (picks, picked, pick•ing) **a.** to choose. *Which poem did you pick to read?* **b.** to pull off. *We can pick cherries from the tree.*

pig (pigs *pl.*) a short animal with a thick body and a flat nose. *Our pig likes to dig.*

pin a. a thin piece of metal with a sharp point. *A pin can hold things together.* **b.** a small piece of jewelry with a sharp point. *Grandmother wore a pretty pin on her dress.*

pine an evergreen tree with leaves like needles. *We found a lot of cones under the tall pine.*

plug a. one end part of an electrical cord. *The lamp will go off if you pull the plug.* **b.** (plugs, plugged, plug•ging) to connect to an electrical outlet. *Please plug in the iron.*

plum a small, soft, juicy fruit. *He picked a wild plum.*

pole a long thin piece of wood or metal. *We hung the flag from a pole.*

pop (pops, popped, pop•ping) to make a short, loud sound. *Did you hear the balloon pop?*

post a wooden or metal pole. *Ted will paint the post.*

pot a deep, round dish or pan. *A pot is used for cooking.*

pumps makes something flow from one place to another. *Mom pumps the gas into our car.*

pup a young dog; a puppy. *The happy pup wagged his tail.*

pup

push (push•es, pushed, push•ing) **a.** to press on something to move it. *Push the gate shut.* **b.** to shove. *Try not to push the people in front of you.*

quack the sound made by a duck. *We heard the quack of the wild duck as it flew south.*

rake a. a garden tool with a long handle, used to gather leaves. *Put the rake in the shed.* **b. (rakes, raked, rak•ing)** to use this tool. *Will you help me rake the leaves?*

ran past tense of **run**. *We ran fast.*

rest a. the other part; what is left over. *I ate ten nuts and Mark ate the rest.* **b.** to stop working; to relax. *Rest a minute before you go on.*

rice a grain that people eat. *We ate chicken and rice.*

ride (rides, rode, rid•den, rid•ing) **a.** to sit on a moving animal or bicycle. *Can you ride a horse?* **b.** to go in a car, bus, or train. *How long does it take to ride to the city?*

rip (rips, ripped, rip•ping) to tear apart. *He may rip his pants on a nail.*

rod a long thin pole of wood, metal, or plastic. *Dad took his fishing rod to the pond.*

233

room **a.** a closed space inside a building. *Jan walked into the front room.* **b.** extra space. *Leave room on your paper for your name.*

rope a strong cord made by twisting smaller cords together. *We used a rope to hang the swing.*

rose a flower that grows on a bush with thorns. *A rose smells sweet.*

rose

rug a covering for a floor; a carpet. *He has a round rug in his room.*

run (runs, ran, run, run•ning) to move quickly; to go faster than walking. *Doug ran to first base.*

rust the coat of red-brown powder that forms on metals when they get damp. *My bike got a spot of rust when I left it outside.*

same just like another; identical. *Do it the same way I do.*

see (sees, saw, seen, see•ing) **a.** to look at; to use the eyes. *I can see a truck on the road.* **b.** to find out. *See if she needs any help.*

seed the part of a plant from which another plant grows. *An acorn is the seed of an oak tree.*

seed

set **a.** a group of things that belong together. *A carpenter needs a set of tools.* **b.** (sets, set, set•ting) to put in a certain place. *Set the dishes on the table.*

shake (shakes, shook, shak•en, shak•ing) to move quickly up and down or from side to side. *The label says "Shake well before using."*

she that girl or woman. *She likes to read.*

ship **a.** a large boat. *The ship sailed across the sea.* **b.** (ships, shipped, ship•ping) to send by boat, truck, or plane. *Our aunt will ship us a crate of apples.*

shop **a.** a small store. *We have a good hobby shop on our street.* **b.** (shops, shopped, shop•ping) to go to stores to buy things. *I'm going to shop for food.*

show (shows, showed, shown or showed, show•ing) **a.** to point out. *I will go first to show the way.* **b.** a movie, play, or TV program. *We saw a funny show.*

shut (shuts, shut, shut•ting) to close. *Will you shut the door, please?*

side **a.** a line that makes an edge. *Trace that side of the triangle.* **b.** the part between the top and the bottom or between the back and the front. *Use the door at the side of the house.*

sip (sips, sipped, sip•ping) to drink slowly, a little at a time. *I like to sip juice with a straw.*

sit (sits, sat, sit•ting) to rest on the lower part of the body. *I will sit in this big chair.*

skip (skips, skipped, skip•ping) to move quickly by hopping twice on each foot. *The children want to skip around the yard.*

slam (slams, slammed, slam•ming) to shut hard with a loud noise. *The wind made the door slam.*

slip (slips, slipped, slip•ping) to slide suddenly. *Don't slip on the wet sidewalk.*

snap (snaps, snapped, snap•ping) **a.** to make a quick bite. *Look at that fish snap at the bait!* **b.** to break or crack. *I can snap this twig in two.*

snug cozy; comfortable. *Coats keep us snug and warm.*

so **a.** very. *I love you so much.* **b.** in the same way; also. *He is a good helper, and so is his sister.*

sock a short stocking. *A long sock comes up to the knee.*

sock

soon before long. *Dinner will be ready soon.*

spin (spins, spun, spin•ning) to turn around fast. *Can you see the wheel spin?*

spoon a tool for eating or serving that has a small bowl at one end. *Bring a spoon for the soup, please.*

step (steps, stepped, step•ping) **a.** a movement of the foot. *Simon says, "Take a big step."* **b.** a small platform for the foot. *I can stand on the top step.* **c.** to lift the foot and put it down in a new place; to walk. *Step to the front of the line.*

stiff not able to bend easily; hard. *My new toothbrush is stiff.*

still **a.** quiet; silent. *The house is very still at night.* **b.** even; yet. *Do you still have that old ball?*

stir (stirs, stirred, stir•ring) to move around or mix. *Jessica can stir the oatmeal with a spoon.*

stool a seat with no back or arms. *Please push the stool under the table.*

stove something you cook on. *The stove is hot.*

sun the star that gives us light and heat. *The sun sets in the west.*

sun

sweep (sweeps, swept, sweep•ing) to clean by brushing away. *Sweep up this dirt with a broom.*

tag **a.** a small piece of paper, metal, or plastic that contains information. *Can you read the price tag?* **b.** a game of chase. *Let's play freeze tag.*

take (takes, took, tak•en, tak•ing) **a.** to grip; to hold. *Take my hand when we cross the street.* **b.** to carry. *Can you take this box to the office?*

tame not wild; gentle. *You can pet the tame animals in the children's zoo.*

that (those *pl.*) the thing or person over there. *Greg sits at that desk by the window.*

the that one or those. *Did you find the pen or the pencils I lost?*

then **a.** at that time. *They came at 2:00, but I was gone then.* **b.** soon after. *We went to the movies, and then we came home.*

thin (thin•ner, thin•nest) not thick or fat. *A sheet of paper is thin.*

this (these *pl.*) the thing or person nearby. *Is this lunch box yours?*

thud a dull sound made when something big falls. *The suitcase fell with a thud.*

thump a loud bumping noise. *Did you hear that thump in the attic?*

tide the regular rise and fall of the water in the sea. *Let's look for seashells at low tide.*

time what a clock shows; the hour and minute. *What time is it?*

time

tip **a.** the end or point. *Can you touch the tip of your nose?* **b. (tips, tipped, tip•ping)** to lean; to push over. *The milk will spill if you tip the glass.*

to as far as; until; toward. *I'll walk to the corner with you.*

top **a.** the highest part. *A bird sat on the top of the tree.* **b.** a cover or lid. *Put the top on the jar, please.*

trot **(trots, trot•ted, trot•ting)** to move at a pace between a walk and a run. *A horse can trot or gallop.*

tub a wide, open container for bathing or washing. *I took a hot bath in the tub.*

tuck **(tucks, tucked, tuck•ing)** to cover or wrap snugly. *I helped tuck the baby in the crib.*

tug **(tugs, tugged, tug•ging)** to pull hard. *My dog likes to tug on his leash.*

twins two persons born to the same mother at the same time. *The twins Don and Ron look alike.*

up in, at, or to a higher place. *The rocket went up into the sky.*

us we; ourselves; the persons talking. *Play with us!*

use **(us•es, used, us•ing)** to put into action; to work with. *Jim will use a hammer to hit the nail.*

vase a bottle or jar used to hold flowers. *Cindy put the roses in a pretty vase.*

vase

vest a short jacket with no sleeves. *My vest matches my pants.*

vine a plant with a long stem that can twist around things. *Grapes grow on a vine.*

wag (**wags, wagged, wag•ging**) to move from side to side. *My dog likes to wag her tail as she eats.*

wake (**wakes, woke** or **waked, waked** or **wo•ken, wak•ing**) to stop or cause to stop sleeping. *Please wake me at six o'clock.*

was past tense of **is**. *He was sick.*

we us; ourselves; the persons speaking. *We are friends.*

weed an unwanted plant that grows wild. *Weeds grow fast.*

wet not dry. *The paint is still wet.*

wide (**wid•er, wid•est**) big from side to side. *A street with four lanes is wide.*

wig a covering of false hair for the head. *I'm going to wear a wig.*

wig

wipe (wipes, wiped, wip•ing) to clean or dry by rubbing. *Wipe the dust off the table.*

wish a. (wish•es, wished, wish•ing) to want; to hope for. *I wish you could come over.* **b.** something you want or hope for. *Did your wish come true?*

with a. in the company of. *They went with Uncle Charles.* **b.** using. *I washed my hands with soap and water.*

woke past tense of **wake**. *The thunder woke us up.*

yes the opposite of **no**. *Yes, you are right.*

yet a. up to now. *They haven't come yet.* **b.** still. *They may get here yet.*

you the person or persons spoken to. *You may go now.*

zip (zips, zipped, zip•ping) to close with a zipper. *Zip your jacket before you go out.*

zoo a place where live animals are kept for people to see. *In the zoo we saw some polar bears.*

zoo

W

Credits